I WAS THERE

The crowd was so large, right down to the water's edge, that Jesus got into a boat and taught them. *Mark 4.1*

I WAS THERE

*The Meaning of the Story of Jesus
told by those who were there*

Peter Sills

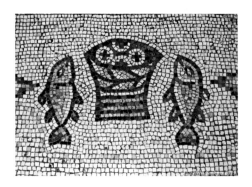

Principal illustrations
Philip Kerrey

Published by Peter Sills Books 2021

www.peter-sills.co.uk

Cover
Jesus calls Zacchaeus
Philip Kerrey

Frontispiece
Jesus teaches at the Lakeside
John Sansom

Title page
Mosaic of the Loaves and Fishes, Church of the Multiplication
of the Loaves and Fishes, Tabgha, Galilee *(author's image)*

ISBN 978-1-8381050-3-7

Printed by Lemonade Print Group, Burgess Hill

CONTENTS

V Passover & Passion

PREFACE

THERE is something compelling about the story of Jesus. It has truth, warmth and humour, drama and tragedy; rightly has it been described as the greatest story ever told, but the meaning of the story is not always explored in the telling, and so in this account, as well as telling the story I explore its meaning. What did the ordinary people feel about Jesus? How did they respond to him? What did the disciples believe about this man they had felt compelled to follow, particularly as his ministry turned from teaching and healing to confrontation? What were the aims and motivations of those who condemned him?

Studying the Bible, growing in faith – any kind of spiritual progress – is not about absorbing information, but making a journey. We will, of course, learn new things, and this is important, but equally important is entering into the story. The journey of faith is primarily one of imagination and empathy. What we learn comes alive when we can see in context and relate it to our own lives. So I have endeavoured to imagine how those who were there at the time experienced the events of Jesus' life, and to tell the story through their eyes. Some of my storytellers are familiar to us from the gospels, for example Jesus' disciples Peter and Andrew; other narrators are those who will have been present but who are not named, for example Jethro, a farmer who listened to Jesus teach at the lakeside; Ehud, one of the scribes who confronted him; or Pontius Pilate's secretary, Gaius Flavius, who observed his trial before Pilate (the names are mine). Whoever they are, I have tried to see the story from their point of view and to understand the meaning it had for them.

Rather than conflate the four gospels into a single story, my account follows the Gospel of Mark. Mark's is a spare account, which has the advantage of giving room for imagination, but sometimes it is a bit too spare, as for example when he writes of the baptism and temptation of Jesus, and so occasionally I have supplemented his story with material from *Luke*.

I hope *I Was There* will be helpful to those who would like to believe in God but hesitate; to those preparing to be confirmed, and to all looking for greater depth in their faith. I hope also that home groups and study groups will find it a good basis for discussion.

I think the best way to use the book is as a daily reflection, rather than reading it through like a novel. For each episode I give the relevant biblical references; these should be read first, preferably in a modern version of the Bible. The 'continuity' paragraph, in which I set the scene and introduce the narrator, links the reading with the text. At the end of each episode it is a good idea to take a few minutes to reflect. You may find it helpful to make a note of what occurs to you, and then offer your response to God in a brief prayer.

However it is approached, my account is a personal response to the story of Jesus, offered to encourage others to imagine what it must have been like to be there at the time, and so enter in heart and mind into the greatest story ever told.

Peter Sills

I am very grateful to Philip Kerrey for the cover and the principal illustrations and to John Sansom for the frontispiece. Special thanks also to Penelope Bennett and Helen Trippe for reading the manuscript and making many helpful comments. I am greatly indebted to them.

*Asterisks * in the text indicate that further information or explanation can be found in an endnote, referenced by page number.*

I

Preparing the Way

Leave your own country and your father's house, and go to a country that I will show you. *Genesis 12.1*

1
PROMISED LAND
Caanan – c2000 BCE

Genesis 12.1-9; 16.1 – 17.8

To enter into the meaning of the story of Jesus we need to begin two thousand years before he was born, going back to the time of Abraham, the great patriarch to whom Israel looks back as its founding father. Abraham made the first of three epic journeys which are basic to the story of Israel and God's call to her, which, Christians believe, was fulfilled in the life and ministry of Jesus.

Abraham was called by God to make a long journey from the Chaldean city of Ur (in modern Iraq) to Canaan (now Palestine/Israel). It was the beginning of the settlement of the Hebrews in what became known as the Promised Land. The story of Abraham is more legend than history,* but that does not mean it lacks truth. Its truth lies chiefly in what it says about God, and the importance of faithfulness to him.* According to the Bible, Abraham was a remote descendant of Noah; ten generations separated them. He married Sarah, who bore him a son Isaac, from whom Jews trace their descent. He also had a son called Ishmael with Hagar, Sarah's slave-girl, from whom Muslims trace their descent. Abraham is therefore an important figure in three faiths: Judaism, Christianity and Islam. It is hard to overstate the importance of Abraham in the religions of the Middle East: he is honoured by Jews, Christians and Muslims alike as the archetypal man of faith.

*After Sarah died, Abraham married Keturah, with whom he had six further sons. The story of his epic journey would have been passed down through the generations, as it is today. **Talia,** the great grand-*

daughter of Eldaah, one of Abraham's sons with Keturah, remembers the story of the family patriarch.

MY great-grandfather, Eldaah, was the child of Abraham's old age. I never knew him, but he feels part of my life, just like Abraham, my great-great-grandfather. I must have been about five when I first heard the story of how the LORD* called him to leave Ur and make a journey to … well, he knew not where. All the LORD said to him was: 'Leave your own country, your kin, and your father's house, and go to a country that I will show you. I shall make you into a great nation; I shall bless you and make your name great.' *[Genesis 12.1–2]*

We're used to travelling. We're always on the move seeking water and pasture for our flocks and herds. We keep to well-known routes, but Abraham's journey was something else. He and his family set off to somewhere far, far away that he'd never heard of! He said goodbye to his home-land and his kin, knowing that he would not see them again. All he had to guide him and keep him going was the LORD'S call and promise that he would be with him, and that through him a great nation would be founded. Abraham believed, and so it was.

Actually, when he set out his name was Abram. It was when he arrived in Caanan that the LORD made a covenant with him and gave him a new name. This is our custom: at significant times, when our life changes and points in a new direction, we take a new name that signifies our new destiny. That's what the LORD'S covenant with Abram was all about, a new destiny; he was to be the father of many nations.

Our names have meanings. My name Talia means 'gentle dew from heaven' – it's a beautiful name, and I love it. Abram means 'high father', in other words, the family patriarch; but Abraham means 'father of a multitude', which is very different! His destiny was revealed by his new name. (At the same time the

LORD gave his wife Sarai the new name Sarah, which means 'princess'.)*

My great-great-grandfather was a real man of faith, and that's why we keep his memory alive, but there were times when his faith was sorely tested, and he must have wondered if the LORD's promise would be fulfilled. For years he had no son – that was why Sarah gave him her slave-girl Hagar as a wife, and he had Ismael with her. But Ismael wasn't a true heir; the LORD said his promise wasn't going to be fulfilled through him. Through whom then? The answer came through three men who visited Abraham when he was living by the oak trees at Mamre. It is part of the nomadic tradition to show kindness to strangers, so he hurried to meet them, bowing before them and entreating them to share a meal. They accepted, and while the meal was being prepared asked about Sarah, and then they said something astonishing: by the same time the following year she will have had a son! Now both of them were well on in years, and Sarah was well past the age of childbearing. She overheard what the men said, and laughed at the idea: she was old and worn out; how could it possibly be?

Well, she may have laughed at the idea, but she *did* have a son! It was the LORD who had visited in the form of the three men, who, they realised later, were angels. And sure enough, a year later when the child was born, the LORD returned and told them to call him Isaac, which means 'laughter'. It's a joke in our family: God had the last laugh! And it happened again with Isaac and his wife Rebecca. For years she couldn't have children; Isaac entreated the LORD, and she conceived. She had twins, my great-uncles Esau and Jacob. God is always true to his promise – even though we can't see how he will fulfil it.

2

EXODUS
Egypt – c1440 BCE

Exodus 1.1-3.12; 12.37 - 14.31

The second epic journey is that of the Exodus, the escape of the Israelites from slavery in Egypt to freedom in the promised land. In this journey Israel sees her beginning as the People of God, and it is commemorated every year at Passover. It took place around 550 years after Abraham, c.1440 BC. This was the time of Moses, the great Hebrew leader, who organised and led the escape.

Several centuries earlier, the Hebrews had fled to Egypt to escape a severe famine in Canaan and the surrounding countries. God had prepared the way through Joseph, the youngest son of Jacob, Abraham's grandson and Talia's great-uncle, another of the Jewish patriarchs. Joseph was a precocious child and his brothers were jealous of him. They conspired against him and treacherously sold him into slavery; he ended up in Egypt. In time, through his gift for interpreting dreams, he found favour with Pharaoh and became his chief minister. He took charge of the arrangements for ensuring Egypt would survive the famine. It was he who welcomed Jacob and the whole tribe of the Hebrews to Egypt (the Joseph saga is told in Genesis chapters 37 - 50). However, many generations later, when a new dynasty who did not know Joseph ascended the throne, the Egyptians turned against the Hebrews and enslaved them. Their plight was dire, and their treatment harsh; eventually they regained their freedom through Moses.

Moses was a Hebrew by birth, but through divine intervention he had been brought up as a prince in the Egyptian royal household. As *an adult he was so moved by the plight of his people that he took up their cause. On one occasion he intervened in a quarrel between an Egyptian overseer and a Hebrew slave, killing the Egyptian. His deed became known and he fled to Midian, where he became a shepherd. One day Moses saw in the desert a bush that seemed to be on fire, but which was not consumed by the fire. He went closer to see this extraordinary sight, and out of the bush he heard God calling his name. He replied, 'Here I am!' And God commissioned him to be the deliverer of his People from slavery (Exodus 3).*

God then sent Moses to Pharaoh to demand that he let the Israelites go in order to worship him, but Pharaoh refused, despite the miraculous acts that Moses performed as signs of his divine authority. And so, according to the Bible, God brought a series of seven plagues, divine acts of judgement, upon Egypt. There were swarms of flies and frogs and locusts, there was hail and pestilence, and the Nile turned to blood, but Pharaoh remained unyielding, and refused to let the people go. God then disclosed to Moses the final disaster he was to bring upon Egypt: the slaughter of all the firstborn of both man and beast. It was an appalling act of judgement. Pharaoh relented, and Moses prepared the people to leave.*

*This second epic journey was the founding event for Israel. Not only did it bring freedom **from** oppression, it also brought freedom **for** worship, and transformed the Hebrews from a rabble of slaves into a people, the People of God (the story is told in Exodus, chapters 1–14). **Caleb**, a young boy at the time, looks back on these momentous events.*

'CALEB! Come on. Get up!'

I can still hear my mother's words as she woke me in the middle of the night. For a week or more there had been a charged atmosphere in the slave camp, even we kids felt it. Something big was happening. I remember mother telling us we were going on a journey to worship God at a special place, but that was all.

I was just coming up to my seventh birthday. The only home I'd known was the slave camp, but one of the Elders had told us children that when we Hebrews first came to Egypt it was as the guests of Pharaoh. It was at a time of famine. Many years before, God had brought it about that our ancestor Joseph became the chief minister to Pharaoh, and he had prepared the way for us. The Elder said that God had rescued us through Joseph. Well, perhaps he had, but that wasn't much comfort. Centuries had passed since Joseph's time, and the Egyptians had turned against us; they resented our presence in their land; resentment had turned to hatred, and now we were their slaves. We'd more or less given up hope; it felt as if God had abandoned us. I don't think many of the adults at the time expected things to change, but I suppose the hope never entirely went away.

And then Moses came. And the hope became real. The LORD sent him to Pharaoh to demand that he let us go: 'Let my people go!' was his cry. We all heard about the signs he had performed before Pharaoh, and, of course we were only too aware of the disasters that were brought upon Egypt. The Elders said it was divine judgement for all the suffering we had endured. They were sure the LORD was about to set us free.

'Caleb. Get up!' My mother repeated, 'We're leaving NOW! Roll up your bed and put it in this bag. I've already got your clothes and other things.'

I don't think she and my father had been to sleep. Everything was piled on a cart, and as soon as I and my brothers and sister were out of the tent, it was quickly collapsed and put on top. And then our long walk to freedom began.

There were thousands of us; it took several days for everyone to leave; fortunately, we were among the first. As we waited I asked my father what had happened. He said that after the final disaster Pharaoh had at last given in.

'The final disaster... what was that?' I asked.

'Death,' he said. 'One morning, a few days ago, when the Egyptians awakened they discovered that all their firstborn had died, children and animals. It was the hand of the LORD.'

'Was that what all that screaming and wailing was about?'

'Yes, it was. They won't dare touch us now.'

So we were able to leave without being pursued. Some days later the news reached us from the guards who were bringing up the rear that the Egyptians had tried to pursue us, but had failed. We had safely crossed an area that floods from time to time – the Sea of Reeds I think it's called* – but when the Egyptians tried to follow, they were caught in a flash flood, and many perished. Father said it was another sign that God was with us!

WELL, I'm an old man now. We finally made it to Canaan. It was a very long journey and took many years; no-one thought it would take as long as it did.* I remember father saying we'd be in Canaan within the year. How wrong he was. He never lived to see the promised land, nor did the other adults, nor Moses himself. It was my generation that Joshua led across the Jordan.

Why did our journey take so long? I remember as I grew up asking that time and again. It was the question on everyone's lips, and we never really got an answer. It wasn't long before Moses had the makings of a rebellion on his hands. We got to the point when slavery in Egypt seemed better than scratching out a miserable existence in Sinai. But looking back, it's clear to me we just weren't ready to conquer the land; not physically, nor spiritually. We had to learn discipline, to become united – we didn't realise just how much slavery had stunted our humanity and our compassion for our fellow Hebrews. But perhaps more importantly, we had to learn what it meant to be God's People. We weren't meant just to be a conquering army, but an example of how God wanted all peoples to live.

The LORD had chosen well when he chose Moses to lead us. He was a father to us like our great ancestor Abraham. The LORD had led him on a journey, too, uprooted him from his homeland, and expected him to journey wherever he was told. Like us, he'd no idea where he was going, but his obedience was counted to him as righteousness. Moses was obedient too – another Abraham, in a way – bringing to completion what the LORD had intended all along. It was through him that we received our laws, our festivals and forms of worship, everything that marks us out from the other nations.

They say that before he died, Moses said: 'The LORD your God will raise up for you a prophet like me from among your own brothers. You must listen to him.' *[Deuteronomy 18.15]* But I wonder if we will see another like him who spoke to the LORD face to face.

3
EXILE
Babylon 597 – 538 BCE

Jeremiah 39.1-10; Isaiah 40.1-5 + 41.1-10

The first two epic journeys were journeys of hope, the third a journey of desolation. At the end of the seventh century BC King Nebuchadnezzar of Babylon moved against Jerusalem, deporting some of its citizens. The city fell in 598/7, and a second deportation followed. In 588 Jerusalem was again besieged and sacked by the Babylonians; Solomon's temple was destroyed and a third deportation to Babylon followed. This devastating experience is recalled in the bitter lament of Psalm 137:

> By the waters of Babylon we sat down and wept
> as we remembered Zion.
> On the willow trees there
> we hung up our lyres,
> for there those who had carried us captive
> asked us to sing them a song,
> our captors called on us to be joyful:
> 'Sing us one of the songs of Zion.'
> How could we sing the LORD'S song
> in a foreign land?   *Psalm 137.1-4*

The Exile occurred around eight centuries after the Exodus. By this time Israel had divided into two kingdoms, Judah in the south, and Israel in the north. Both kingdoms looked back to the reign of King David (1010-970 BC) as a golden age. David had followed in the ways of the LORD, but later kings did not, turning away from God, and following the ways of the world. Prophets arose, beginning with the great Elijah in the 9th century BC, who denounced false ways and called both kings and people back to God. Their warnings went unheeded, and the northern kingdom was conquered by Assyria in 721 BC, and many of the people were taken into Exile. God, it was believed, was punishing them for turning away from him.

History was repeated when the southern kingdom of Judah was conquered by King Nebuchadnezzar of Babylon, and its leading citizens deported, as mentioned above. Caleb's distant descendants, who had become members of the royal court in Jerusalem, were among those deported to Babylon. During their captivity, a gifted prophet arose, and much later, when the Jewish scriptures were brought together, the editors noted the similarity of his oracles to those of Isaiah of Jerusalem (who had lived two centuries earlier), and incorporated his prophecy into the Book of Isaiah. The prophet is known as Second Isaiah, or Isaiah of Babylon. He spoke words of comfort to the exiles; their captivity was coming to an end:

> Comfort, comfort my people;
>   - it is the voice of your God;
> speak tenderly to Jerusalem
>   and tell her this,
> that she has fulfilled her term of bondage,
>   that her penalty is paid;
> she has received at the Lord's hand
> double measure for all her sins.   *Isaiah 40.1- 2*

As well as assuring the people the exile was coming to an end, the 'new Isaiah' spoke about God in new ways. The LORD, he said, is not like the gods of the nations; he is the only God, the God of all the nations. He loves and cares for his people; he will come among them and bear their burdens, taking their suffering upon himself. Isaiah of Babylon also reminded Israel of her destiny: God had chosen her not for privilege, but for service, to make his ways known to all nations. Speaking in the name of the LORD, he made this clear:

> It is too slight a task for you, as my servant,
> to restore the tribes of Jacob,

> to bring back the descendants of Israel:
> I will make you a light to the nations,
> to be my salvation to earth's farthest bounds.   *Isaiah 49.6*

*Not everyone accepted Isaiah of Babylon's prophecies, but some took them to heart, among them **Terah**, one of Caleb's descendants. Terah deals with a Babylonian official called **Reza** on behalf of the Jewish exiles. One day their conversation took an unexpected turn, and Terah found himself explaining what the new Isaiah had said.*

I WAS quite taken aback. The Reza I'd got to know was a typical official: reserved, efficient and unemotional; a bit of a cold fish. Although I'd never felt from him the contempt that some royal officials had for us exiles, there was more than a hint of disdain. Even so, still waters run deep: one day, out of the blue, he said, 'Terah, we're always talking about food and supplies, but there's something else I'd like to ask you, something that really puzzles me about you Israelites. It's about your religion and your god.'

This was the last thing I'd expected. 'Rather different to your god, Marduk,' I said.

'Well, you tell me,' he replied. 'Marduk is a mighty warrior, the supreme Lord of the gods of heaven and earth. All creation owes its existence to him, and the destiny of kingdoms and subjects is in his hands. Don't you think of your god in the same way – whatever you call him? You know, I've never heard any of you speak his name.'

I explained that His name is too sacred to be spoken, so we refer to him simply as the LORD. But what else could I say? True, we believed the LORD to be the creator of the world and the Lord of destiny, but that's where the similarity ended. I'd heard a bit about Marduk, and the Babylonian story of creation, which was totally different to what we believed. They believed there were many gods, and that creation was the outcome of war among them – Marduk actually killing his mother and creating the cosmos from her corpse.* How do you begin to speak to people who believe this kind of stuff?

'Well,' I said, 'it's true we believe the LORD to be almighty, the creator of all that is, but for us, creation was born from an act of love, not violence.' I told him the story of Adam and Eve: how the LORD made man from the dust of the earth, and placed him in a garden of delight, and from him created woman to be his companion. 'That's where love comes from,' I added.

Reza looked up as though insight had just dawned. 'I see,' he said, 'that makes sense. The LORD is not a warrior like Marduk, so no wonder we conquered you. You should get yourself a better god!'

'Well, this will be a puzzle to you,' I said, 'but we don't want another God. We look at life differently to you. Life is more than conflict, and power is more than violence. The LORD *is* a God of power – he freed us from slavery in Egypt – but he's also a God of justice. His vision is of heaven on earth, for people to live together in peace, not continually fighting. The LORD is not just our champion, he is also our judge, and when we forget his vision of peace, he lets us know. This exile is his judgement upon us. We have not followed his ways, and he has allowed you to conquer us to teach us a lesson.'

Reza's expression turned from insight to incomprehension: 'What? He allowed us to conquer you? No way! We conquered you because Marduk is more powerful than your Lord. He had nothing to do with it.'

I wasn't surprised at his reaction. Our view of God was unique; no other people seemed to share it, and that was why we Hebrews were a people set apart. If your rule of life is that might is right, then you would react as Reza had done, but I couldn't leave it there.

'Well, Reza, I said it would be a puzzle, but I need to explain a bit more.'

'Alright,' he replied, indicating he was willing to listen. So, I explained how we thought the LORD had something to do with our captivity.

'You see, the LORD is righteous; that's really the difference between us. You offer sacrifices to Marduk, and it's true we also offer them to the LORD, but some of our prophets have said that sacrifices are not what he requires. What is really pleasing to him is that we act justly, love loyalty, and walk humbly before him.* What he wants is a righteous life. You can't say that about Marduk.'

'Righteous life…? What's that all about?'

'Doing the right thing; living by the LORD'S commandments; treating other people as you would like to be treated yourself.'

Reza interrupted, a note of condescension in his voice: 'But that wouldn't work – look at the mess it's got you in! What works is power. Getting other people to do what you want.'

'OK,' I said, 'but where does that get you? A few have a good life; most live in misery. Don't you have any idea of justice?'

'Justice? You mean enforcing the laws of the king?'

'No! I mean making sure everyone is cared for; making sure they feel that they are part of Israel. That's one of the foundations of the Law that the LORD gave us.'

'Feeling part of Israel? I don't think I'll ever understand you Israelites!

'And there's another thing. We believe that there are many gods, and that Marduk is the Lord of the gods, but you deny this; you say there is only one god, and he is God of all the nations. You've got a prophet, here in Babylon, who says so, the one you call the new Isaiah. I heard him myself: "Thus says the Lord... I am the first and I am the last, and there is no god but me."' *[Isaiah 44.6]*

I was alarmed to hear 'Isaiah of Babylon' (as we called him) had been overheard. Views like that could lead to trouble.

'Does that concern you?' I asked, trying not to sound anxious.

'No, not for a moment,' Reza replied. 'The man must be mad. No, I just wanted to see if this is how you all think. You don't believe him, do you?'

'Well, we don't all think as he does. But I'm beginning to think he's right.'

'Good God, man! Why? Are you going mad too?'

'Well, it may sound odd to you, Reza, but I don't think you've ever known captivity. It affects the way you see things. At first you feel angry and resentful – the squalid conditions, always hungry, the misery of being forced to live far from your homeland – and many just give in to anger and bitterness. They feel totally abandoned by the LORD, and turn away from him in despair and hopelessness. But others, like our new Isaiah, even though they too feel it all, aren't imprisoned by bitterness and despair; somehow they manage to transcend it, and that gives hope to the rest of us. If the LORD is righteous and not capricious, then what's happening to us must have some purpose in his sight.'

Reza looked increasingly uncomprehending as I spoke. He asked what I thought was the purpose of our captivity in the eyes of the LORD: 'Why is he punishing you?'

'I don't think punishment is quite the right word. How can I put it? We've known exile before – when we were overcome by the Assyrians. Then Isaiah – the first one – said the disaster had come upon us because we had forsaken the LORD. I don't think he believed the exile was willed by God as a punishment;

it was a consequence of what we did, and the LORD used it to bring us to our senses. And that's how this new Isaiah sees what is happening to us now.'*

'Well, Terah, I don't pretend to follow you – your LORD sounds a strange kind of god to me. And according to this new Isaiah he is going to act through a servant. Who is this servant: a lesser god, a divine messenger?'

'I think the servant is someone whom the LORD will send – a prophet – who will act on his behalf ... as though he were the LORD himself.'*

'So, when will this servant come?'

'He doesn't say. But what he does say is that the servant will take our sufferings on himself, he will bear the punishment for our iniquities, and that will be the way we are reconciled to the LORD. He put it memorably: "The chastisement he bore will be health for us, and by his scourging we are healed."' *[Isaiah 53.5]*

'And that's God, he's talking about?'

'Yes, I believe so.'

'God suffers in our place?'

'Yes.'

'What kind of a God is that? And how does that fit with him punishing you? I give up! Go in peace, Terah. You Hebrews and your religion are beyond me!'

Isaiah of Babylon's prophecy that the Exile was coming to an end was fulfilled when Babylon fell to the Persians in 539 BC, and the Israelites began to return to Jerusalem. But his oracles about the Servant of God were ignored, and after the return from exile the old ideas about racial and religious exclusivity were enforced by Nehemiah. However, Isaiah of Babylon was not the only one to foresee that God would come among his people in a new way.

Jeremiah, who was not among those deported and remained in Jerusalem, had the same vision:

> A ruler shall appear, one of themselves, a governor shall arise from their own number. I myself shall bring him near and so he shall approach me, says the LORD. So you shall be my people and I will be your God.
>
> *Jeremiah 30.21 - 22*

It was many centuries before these prophecies were fulfilled. In the meantime, after the return from exile, Israel was again overrun by conquering armies, first from Greece and later from Rome. Those who led the resistance became local heroes, like Judas Maccabaeus, one of the leaders of the Maccabean Revolt against the Greek Seleucid Empire (167-160 BC). It was during this period that the belief in the resurrection of the dead arose, largely because it was unthinkable that God would allow heroes like Judas Maccabaeus to perish for ever. Like Isaiah of Babylon's idea of the Servant, this was another strand in the new thinking about God. These new ideas required a focus if they were to take hold; the decisive event which provided that focus was the coming of Jesus, heralded by the miraculous birth of the long-awaited forerunner.

By the waters of Babylon we sat down and wept (Psalm 137)

4
FORERUNNER
Jerusalem – 29 CE

Luke 1 + 3.1-20

*By the time of Jesus, messianic expectation was widespread in Israel. It was believed that the coming of the Messiah would be heralded by the return of the great prophet Elijah. Jesus was asked about this by the three disciples who were with him at the Transfiguration: 'Why do the scribes say that Elijah must come first?' He replied that Elijah would come first to set everything right, and then he added: 'I tell you Elijah has already come and they have done to him what they wanted as the scriptures say of him.' (Mark 9.11-13) Jesus was referring to John the Baptist whom King Herod had beheaded (Mark 6.14-29). John would have been about six months older than Jesus; Luke tells us that he was Jesus' cousin (that is, a member of the extended family, not necessarily what we mean by 'cousin' today), and that his birth was miraculous; but he says nothing more about John's early years. However, as he was the child of his parents' old age, they would have died early in his life. As his ministry began when he was about thirty years old he must, like Jesus, have had an occupation before then, but what it was is unknown. Following Luke's account, **John the Baptist** tells the story of his call to be a prophet.*

PRIESTHOOD runs in families. My father, Zechariah, was a priest, and so was his father before him, and his father... and so on as far back as we can remember – I expect as far back as Moses who established the priesthood, and laid down all the rules and rituals for worship. But this tradition came to an end with me. When I was a young boy I and my friends assumed that after my bar-mitzvah I would begin my training for the priesthood, but as the time drew near nothing had been said about it. My mother had died the previous year, and my father was well on in years, and had become quite forgetful, but sooner or later, I thought, I'll have to ask him about it. But he hadn't forgotten. Out walking one day, we rested in a shady spot overlooking the city – it was one of his favourite places.

'Well, John,' he said, 'this is your bar-mitzvah year. You will soon become a son of the law; all its rights will be yours, and also its duties. It's a very special time for any man, but for you it will be extra special. I've been waiting for this moment. I talked about it with your mother before she died, and we agreed that this would be right time to tell you about what happened when you were born.'

I knew that something unusual had happened. My parents were very much older than those of my cousins – an aunt of my mother's had said something about God at last taking away my mother's shame,* though he'd taken his time about it! She said my father had been dumfounded at my birth, but it wasn't until he told me about his vision of the angel, and how he had literally been struck dumb, that I really understood what she had meant. And, of course, it explained why I was called John when no one else in our family had that name. John means 'Yahweh is gracious'. It was a wonderful name to have, but I didn't know quite what to make of what my father said next.

'You see, John, your birth was a gracious sign from the Lord. You being the child of our old-age – nothing less than a miracle – it made me realise that God was doing a new thing. He was bringing about a new beginning, not only for your mother and me, but also for Israel. I can still remember what the angel said to me about you:

He will bring gladness to many,
for he will be great in the eyes of the Lord...
From his very birth he will be filled with the Holy Spirit;
and he will bring back many Israelites
  to the Lord their God.
He will go before him as a forerunner,
possessed by the spirit and power of Elijah,
to reconcile father and child,
to convert the rebellious to the ways of the righteous,
to prepare a people that shall be fit for the Lord.'

[Luke 1.14 –17]

'He said that about me?' I spluttered, not knowing quite what to make of it.

'Yes, John; he said it about you.'

'So, does that mean I'm not going to be a priest like you?'

'Yes, it does. I've been talking to Naboth. You can work on his farm until the LORD calls you to fulfil your destiny.'

I helped my father to his feet and we continued our walk. I was coming up to thirteen; at that age I was a bit confused, not knowing quite what to make of it. 'Fulfilling my destiny' sounded a bit scary – and also a bit exciting – but what did it mean? And those words of the angel: what did they mean? After a few days the feeling wore off, and we got on with life. I celebrated my bar-mitzvah and went to work for Naboth.

It wasn't long afterwards that my father died, and I went to live with Naboth. This, too, was unusual. Normally, a boy in my situation would live with someone in the family, but, looking back on it, the LORD had begun to take a more direct rôle in my life. Naboth wasn't just a farmer, he was also the senior elder in the synagogue, and he continued my education in the scriptures – no one in our family could have done this. The turning point came one day when we were studying the

Book of Isaiah. I mentioned that Isaiah was one of my heroes; Naboth's response took me by surprise.

'Is he, now. Which Isaiah?'

'What do you mean? Was there more than one?'

'Yes. There must have been more than one because the Book covers more than two centuries. The one it's named after was Isaiah of Jerusalem. He served under four kings: from Uzziah to Hezekiah *[742 – 701 BC]*. The names of the other two 'Isaiahs' are not known. The second one had the most original mind; I call him Isaiah of Babylon, because he was a prophet during the Exile.'*

'What was so original about him?'

'It was given to him to see deep into the heart of God. He spoke of God as a servant, not a lord – a servant who cared for his people as well as being judge over them.'

'I've never heard that before. Are you sure?'

'Quite sure. Next sabbath, after the service, you can see for yourself. I'll show you the scroll.'

And that's what he did. It opened my eyes. Isaiah of Babylon spoke towards the end of the Exile. He assured the captives that Israel had paid her penalty; her captivity was coming to an end. As we read through the scroll, I began to see that he pictured God as love, not wrath. And yes, he did say that God would come to his people as a servant; he would bear their burdens and take their suffering on himself. Together, we read the four 'songs' in which Isaiah describes the Servant. In the longest one the suffering of the Servant is made plain: he will be despised and rejected by men; they won't understand that he was sent by God. I had heard the words before, but this time I began to take them to heart:

> Yet on himself he bore our sufferings,
>   our torments he endured,

while we counted him smitten by God,
    struck down by disease and misery;
but he was pierced for our transgressions,
    tortured for our iniquities;
the chastisement he bore was health for us
    and by his scourging we are healed.
We had all strayed like sheep,
    each of us had gone his own way;
but the Lord laid upon him
    the guilt of us all.   *[Isaiah 53.4–6]*

I turned to Naboth: 'I've never thought of love like that – bearing another's sins, suffering the punishment they deserve. Why does God do that?'

'Because that's what love does, and that's what forgiveness is all about. Love reaches out to others, wants everyone to be included.'

We looked at another 'song' in which Isaiah re-interpreted the destiny of Israel in terms of reaching out to others. Naboth read from the scroll:

It is too slight a task for you, as my servant,
to restore the tribes of Jacob,
    to bring back the descendants of Israel:
I will make you a light to the nations,
to be my salvation to earth's farthest bounds.   *[Isaiah 49.6]*

Isaiah's message was clear: God chose us not for privilege, but for service. God's purpose for Israel is to make him known to the nations. Questions welled up in my mind. 'If that's how God is, why haven't I heard the Rabbi say anything like that?'

'Well, John, Isaiah's vision was a new picture of God, and it's still a new picture. I'm not sure what effect Isaiah's words had at the time, but they were forgotten when the Exile ended, and since then they have not fitted with accepted ideas. That's why, I guess, we don't hear about it.'

'Does Isaiah say anything about the Messiah?'

'No; not as such. The idea of the Messiah came later, but right from the beginning there has been an expectation that our story would come to a point of fulfilment. We believe that God, who so wonderfully saved his people from disaster in the Exodus, and then rescued them from Exile, did so because he had a greater purpose for us in mind. It's there in Isaiah's prophecy: Israel's destiny is to make God known to the nations. Was this to be through another prophet like Moses, or another king like David? You can see how the idea of the Messiah arose.'

'Isn't Elijah meant to return as his forerunner?'

'Yes he is. The prophet Malachi said he would return before the day of the LORD.'*

'We're living in those days, aren't we?'

'Yes, John, I believe we are. Elijah must soon return.'

'ELIJAH must soon return.' It was as Naboth had said. The expectation that the Messiah would come was everywhere. That night I had a dream. I was standing by the River Jordan, at the place where Elijah had parted from Elisha. They were talking. And then, all of a sudden, the chariot of Israel and its horsemen swept down from heaven and gathered up Elijah. His cloak fell from him as the clouds parted and he was lost to sight. I looked around. Elisha had disappeared. I ran to where the cloak had fallen, picked it up, and wrapped myself in it.*

I awoke with a start, chilled and trembling. The dream had been so real. I cried out: 'Who am I LORD, God of Israel, that you should call me? I'm not a prophet, nor the son of a prophet; I'm a humble man; I work on the land.' As I prayed, I felt my heart was on fire, stirred in my depths, and I heard a voice speaking to me:

> From before the womb I called you
> to be a prophet of the Most High.
> You will be the forerunner of my chosen One,
> going before him to prepare his way,
> leading his people to a knowledge of salvation
> through the forgiveness of their sins. *[Cf. Luke 1.76–77]*

There was no going back. Like Amos, I had been called from my work on the land to prepare the harvest of the LORD. Naboth accepted my decision to leave him without demur – it felt as though he had long expected it. The LORD called me apart, to a life in the wilderness to prepare for my ministry. Amos, another farmer turned prophet, would be my model; like him I would call the people to repentance. Locust beans and wild honey became my food, and a rough coat of camel's hair my robe. I had indeed been 'graced by God.'

John's influence was widespread. In him the prophetic tradition was re-born, and he is a pivotal figure in the Christian story. Jesus described him as 'far more than a prophet', nothing less than the herald of the new age that Isaiah had prophesied (Luke 7.26-27). John attracted a personal following, and, it seems that his disciples followed a more ascetic way than Jesus's disciples (Luke 5.33-35). Until John was arrested by King Herod Antipas, he and Jesus had parallel ministries; Jesus seems to have taken John's arrest as the sign that his own ministry was to begin in earnest. Mark says it was 'After John had been arrested [that] Jesus came into Galilee proclaiming the gospel of God...' (Mark 1.14)

The widespread sense that a new beginning for Israel was about to dawn was correct. The picture of God given by Isaiah of Babylon, that so appealed to Naboth, may not have been taken to heart by Israel, but Jesus did take it to heart. His followers used Isaiah's picture of God the Servant to interpret Jesus' life and ministry, and, above all, his death. It was nothing less than a re-interpretation of the whole story of Israel.

II
From the Jordan to Galilee

Come, follow me, and I will make you fishers of men. *Mark 1.17*

5
AT THE JORDAN *29 CE*

Mark 1.1-11; Luke 3.1-22

Mark begins his story by the banks of the river Jordan with a brief account of the ministry of John the Baptist. Both Mark and Luke simply say that John 'appeared in the wilderness.' Luke dates it to the fifteenth year of the Emperor Tiberius; John would have been about 30 years of age. Mark does not say where John was baptising, but the fourth gospel says it was at Bethany beyond Jordan, which is in Judea, in the south of Israel, not far from the Dead Sea. Jesus' home was in Nazareth in Galilee, in the north, so at some time he will have made the journey south.

Mark says John the Baptist came in fulfilment of the prophecy of Isaiah of Babylon:

I am sending my herald ahead of you; he will prepare your way.
A voice cries in the wilderness, 'Prepare the way for the Lord;
clear a straight path for him. *Isaiah 40.3*

The prophet Malachi had also foretold that the Lord would come among his people, and that his herald would go ahead of him:

I will send my herald to clear a path before me. *Malachi 3.1*

John was that herald. He proclaimed a baptism in token of repentance for the forgiveness of sins, and he demanded that those he baptised reformed their lives to show that their repentance was real. He announced the imminent coming of one mightier than himself, who would baptise, not with water, but with the Holy Spirit.

John's call to repentance received a ready response. Mark says that people 'flocked to him' from the countryside of Judea and from

Jerusalem, and they were baptised in the river Jordan, confessing their sins (Mark 1.5).

*Amos and his wife Sarah were amongst those who were baptised on the same day as Jesus. The next day **Sarah** visited her friend **Rachel** to tell her all about it.*

Hello Sarah! Come in. Gosh, you look lit up! What's happened? Where have you been?

Oh, Rachel! I've so much to tell you! We went to the Jordan yesterday...

What – to see the prophet John?

Yes. It was amazing!

My brother went the other day. He said the same. He came back quite transformed, but I couldn't get much out of him.

Do tell me what happened. Were there lots of people? How did you feel? I bet it was it wonderful!

It was more than wonderful – it's hard to find the words – but something quite amazing happened. There was a big crowd. John spoke to us, and then, while we all were waiting to be baptised, this man stepped forward. Goodness, did he have a presence about him! Even John seemed a bit in awe of him, and John's an impressive man!

Do you know who he was?

Someone said he was Joshua bar Joseph, from Nazareth.

Nazareth?

Yes. He'd come a long way. Well, John baptised him, just like everyone else, and, as he came up out of the water there was... well... I can only describe it as a sign from heaven. It was like a shaft of light which alighted on Joshua's head, and then... then there was a sound... like a voice. We all heard it. I didn't catch the words, but Amos did. The voice said: 'You are my beloved Son; in you I take delight.'

Say that again.

'You are my beloved Son; in you I take delight.'

Good heavens! That's incredible! And scary! So where did this voice come from? Could you see who it was?

It wasn't anyone in the crowd. There was just the shaft of light. We were all overawed, you could hear the intake of breath... you could feel the silence. And then the voice came. It sent shivers up my spine. I don't know where it came from – it seemed to come from above, from a cloud.

That's awesome! Scary! You read about this kind of thing in the scriptures, but you don't expect it to happen today. Isn't this what happened to Moses? Didn't he hear a voice at the burning bush: 'Take off your sandals; you're standing on holy ground'?

Gracious! I hadn't thought of that. But, yes, Moses all over again.

What did you make of it? Do you think it was the voice of God?

I'm not sure. How do I know what the voice of God sounds like? Maybe it was like Moses, but how do you know? Anyway, there was a stunned silence, everyone looking at Joshua. He stood for a moment on the river bank – you could feel his spirit, like an aura around him. He knelt and prayed, and then he walked away. The crowd just parted and let him through. The silence lasted a long time, but gradually, we all found our voices, and then everyone was talking about it – excited, amazed, bewildered. We'd never seen – or heard – anything like it!

Gosh, you're all lit up as you speak. I can see from your face what it must have been like. As you were speaking a shiver went up my spine too! So who is this Joshua from Nazareth?

I think it's clear that John thinks he is the Messiah.

Really! You know lots of people think John is the Messiah.

I know; I did too. Someone asked him, but he said 'No!' There was one coming after him – one who was mightier than him, and he wasn't fit even to untie the straps of his sandals. He would baptise with the Holy Spirit. Well, after what we'd seen and heard, everyone felt that John was right: Joshua bar Joseph must be the one… the Messiah.

Oh! Sarah! Do you really think so? Has the time that we've been waiting for all these years really come? Are we going to get rid of all these Romans and live again free, as God's People?

I hope so, Rachel. My heart yearns for that! Everything that John says points that way. I think John is the promised Elijah, the forerunner who will prepare the way for the Messiah. He even looks like Elijah, with his rough coat and leather belt, and his very direct way of speaking.

Do you know what he said? He called us a 'viper's brood', and warned us to prove our repentance by changing our lives. 'Don't think it's enough to be descended from Abraham; that won't get you to heaven,' he said. 'No; sort out your lives, turn away from evil and do good. Share your food and clothes with those in need.' He told the tax men to give up cheating, and the soldiers to stop bullying – and to make do with their pay. We loved that!

Yes, I can imagine it! But John sounds just like that prophet Amos. It feels as though he thinks something big is about to happen. Perhaps the New Age is about to dawn, and he's preparing us.

I must go myself. Sarah, I've felt for some time that we're on the verge of something new, something wonderful… lots of people feel it. I must go.

*The next day Rachel went to the Jordan and was herself baptised by John; on her return she went to see Sarah and Amos. Sarah was out at the market and Rachel was greeted by **Amos.***

'Come in Rachel. Just back from the Jordan? You must be tired – it's a long walk. Come in, sit yourself down. I expect you'd like a drink.'

'Thanks, Amos. Yes, some water would be wonderful.' Sarah was tired, but her spirit was alive with her experience. Her mind full of it, she sank gratefully into a chair.

Amos returned: 'Sarah will be here soon. How was it?'

'I don't know quite what I expected, but I found it very moving. It was just as Sarah said, but no Joshua today. As John poured the water over me the tears were streaming down my face. I don't know quite how to put it... I felt renewed, clean, as though a new path had opened up for me.'

'Yes, I know what you mean. We felt the same... it's hard to describe.'

'You know how John begins, calling everyone to repent, to be honest about their sins, and asking if you want, deep down, to turn away from them and lead a new life. Well... I'd wondered what I would say. It's not like I'm a wicked sinner. I try to lead a good life. I do cut corners a bit – well, we all do – but nothing serious. But then he said: "What's at the centre of your life? Is it God or yourself? Do you share your food and your clothes with the needy, or is it you and your needs that always come first? God is about to do a new thing: he has sent his Servant to dwell among us; to lead us to new life, just as Isaiah foretold. But if we're going to recognise him, we need to put away all selfish desires, all self-concern, and look to God alone. To be part of God's new beginning we must be new people. God must be at the centre of our life. Repent. Turn to God in your hearts, and if you do, when I baptise you, God will wash away all that separates you from him."'

Amos remembered John's words well. They had really struck a chord with him. 'Yes, he said much the same to us. What did you make of it?'

'You know, Amos, I'd never thought of sin quite like that before – not putting God at the centre of our life. I'd thought of sin as the things we do wrong, you know, theft, murder, adultery, dishonesty, telling lies – all those things in the Ten Commandments. I hadn't done anything like that, but I realised I was a bit selfish; life revolved around me and my wants. God got a look-in on the Sabbath, but he wasn't really at the centre of my life. And I realised there and then that that's what I'm missing, and I just burst into tears – I wasn't the only one. So when it was my turn to be baptised, I said that to John, and as he poured the water over me, I felt my self-concern being washed away. It was wonderful! I felt like a new person.'

While they were speaking Sarah had returned from the market and had stood at the door, unnoticed. Rachel's feelings were the same as hers. 'We felt the same,' she said, as she joined them.

'Oh! Sarah. I didn't see you there.'

'Sorry, I didn't want to interrupt. Like you, Amos and I felt a bit stuck in a rut. Life didn't seem to have much to offer. Our faith seemed a bit stuck too, if I'm honest. We were wondering: what's the point of it all? So we went to the Jordan hoping for something new, something to lift our spirits. I can feel it all again; as John poured the water over us it *was* like being washed clean, being given a new start.'

'The wonderful thing,' said Amos, 'was that it happened at the Jordan, at the river that's the life-blood of Israel. As its waters poured over my head and down my body I felt they were giving me, giving us, new life and hope.

Sarah asked if there had been any talk about Joshua bar Joseph?'

'Oh yes! Everyone was talking about it,' Rachel replied. 'We'd all heard what happened yesterday, and were hoping to see him, but he wasn't there. I met some people from Nazareth

– you know, where he comes from – they called him by his Greek name, Jesus. They said he was born at the time of the census, in Bethlehem, his father Joseph's home town. They said it was at the same time that a big star appeared in the sky. I hadn't heard about that, had you?'

Something stirred in Sarah's memory. She had forgotten about it, but yes, she did remember. 'Oh! Yes, that's right,' she said. 'I was very young at the time, but I remember my parents talking about it. Amos, you remember these things better than me.'

'Yes, I remember it. My father was a bit of a stargazer. He said it wasn't actually a star, but two planets, Jupiter and Saturn, coming together so they looked like one very bright star. He said it was awesome, and disturbing; everyone was scared. What did it mean? The astrologers said it was an omen, the sign of a new king. But nothing came of it.'

Sarah wasn't so sure that nothing had come of it. 'Well, Amos, if it happened when Joshua was born, maybe it *was* a sign. Kings have to grow up before they can reign. What happened yesterday makes you think. Clearly, there's something very special about him. The way John spoke, I'd say he believes he is the Messiah, and lots of the others said the same.'

Amos hesitated. 'I'd like to believe it, but we've been here before. Others have come claiming to be the Messiah, and our hopes have been raised, only to be dashed. I'm not sure.'

Sarah was surprised; she thought Amos felt the same as her. 'What! even after what we saw yesterday. And the voice: "You are my beloved Son; in you I take delight." What more do you want? None of the others have been hailed from heaven as the Son of God!'

'I do hope you're right. We'll just have to wait and see.'

6

IN THE WILDERNESS

Mark 1.12-13; Luke 4.1-13

After Jesus was baptised, Mark simply records that 'the Spirit drove him out into the wilderness, and there he remained for forty days tempted by Satan.'* Details of the three temptations are added by Luke; each of them offered a way in which Jesus might achieve his aims. Whether or not Jesus decided to follow Satan's advice depended on whom he understood himself to be.

Messiah means the 'anointed one'. It was a title given to the kings of Israel who were believed to be God's anointed vice-regents. After the monarchy ended, and Israel was ruled by foreign powers (who sometimes installed puppet kings like Herod), the expectation grew that the Messiah would come and restore the kingdom, and that he would be a true king from the House of David. Matthew says Jesus was 'born of David's line'; in the wilderness he may have asked himself if his messianic destiny was to be a king? Was this God's way? Or should he follow another path? Jesus used the enigmatic phrase 'Son of Man' to refer to himself. It comes from the prophet Daniel, and has messianic associations, but Jesus never accepted the title of Messiah; his conception of the rôle was very different to the popular idea of a military/political figure.

The time Jesus spent in the wilderness was crucial to his self-understanding, and **James***, who, with Peter and John, was one of the 'inner three' disciples who accompanied Jesus on special occasions like the Transfiguration, tells how Jesus was tempted to follow the ways of the world, and why he rejected them.**

THERE was one occasion I'll never forget when John and I were put in our places by Jesus.* We'd asked if we could have the places of honour next to him when he came into his glory. The others were furious – mostly because they also wanted the seats of honour. Jesus knew this and rebuked us all. We were not to follow the ways of the world, he said, where people sought privilege and the greatest lorded it over the least; no, if we wanted to be great we must learn to be servants; if we wanted to be first, we must become the slaves of all. It didn't make much sense to us, but this conviction lay at the heart of his understanding of what it meant to be the Messiah. He had had to work this out himself. It was in the long time of solitary prayer he had spent in the wilderness after he was baptised that it came to him. God had chosen him, so it was imperative that he saw things truly as God saw them. He said he felt compelled to take time out to pray. The Spirit moved him – no, the way he put it was more powerful than that – the Spirit drove him into solitude, away from family and friends, because from then on he had to learn to depend on God alone and to do things his way. There's a verse in the Psalms that he told us to take to heart:

On God alone my soul in stillness waits;
from him comes my salvation. [Psalm 62.1]

In was in the wilderness that Jesus saw that the Messiah was called be a servant and not a king, nor a conquering hero. This stood accepted ideas on their head, and it took us a long time to get on to his wavelength – I don't think we really did until after he was raised.

At the time everyone was talking about the Messiah. We wanted a leader who would fight for Israel and lead her again to victory and to glory. The temptation for Jesus to take this path came quietly, subtly. One of the things I learnt from him is that this is the way of Satan; it's all done gently: a quiet word in your ear, tempting you along your strengths. This rang bells with me. Once, when John and I had to sort out a problem with the other fishermen, a little demon whispered in my ear: 'Take the quick way to get what you want; impose your will. What you want to do is clearly right and good; just get on with it. You may have to cut a few corners, but the end justifies the means.' So we did. We were strong characters and it was easy to get our way, but it didn't work, and the solution we imposed fell apart. It was an important lesson: the wrong means pervert the end.

Well, in the wilderness the same demon whispered in Jesus' ear, tempting him also along his strengths: 'Whatever you do, you'll need to get the people on your side, otherwise you're doomed to fail. If I were you I'd meet their needs. They're hungry, just like you are now. You're the Son of God, you could make bread out of all these stones. Think of it: free bread. They'd love you for that!'

You see, Jesus did meet people's needs; wherever he went people cried out to him to help them. On one occasion, quite miraculously, he provided food for a huge crowd, but he was always moving on. We didn't get it at first, but he insisted that the greater need was to preach the gospel, to teach the people about the love of God. Meeting needs is good – God does not want people to go hungry or thirsty, or without clothes or shelter – but it's not his priority. The people may love you for a while if you give them bread, but then what? After bread the demands would come thick and fast; they'd never be satisfied. Was the Messiah just meant to meet the people's material needs – and feed their greed? God's priority, said Jesus, is to feed our spirits, to help us grow in faith, trust, compassion and generosity, putting the needs of others before the needs of self. The demon was tempting Jesus to become like a politician, buying favour by offering handouts. This wasn't God's way.

As it says in the scriptures, 'Man is not to live on bread alone. 'And with these words Jesus sent the demon packing!

But the demon did not give up that easily – actually I don't think he ever gives up. He tried a different tack. He gave Jesus a vision of all the kingdoms of the world and whispered: 'All this is yours by divine right, isn't it? Think what you could achieve, all the good you could do, if *you* were the emperor and not Tiberius. Be practical. You need power to get things done; dreaming won't build the kingdom. I know about power; this is my world. It will be much easier if you follow my way: worship me, and all this will be yours. I can give you all the power you need.'

One of the twelve, Simon the Zealot, had similar ideas. The Zealots thought of themselves as practical men, prepared to use force if necessary to do things God's way – or so they thought. Once when Simon was advocating this approach, Jesus rounded on him. Yes, he needed power to be effective, but military and economic power was not the way to capture the hearts of men and women. The only power that could do that was the power of love; this was God's power, and only He was worthy of worship. He rebuked Simon as he had rebuked the demon: 'You shall do homage to the Lord your God, and worship him alone.'

The demon tried one more time, more subtly than before. He took Jesus in his imagination and placed him on the pinnacle of the Temple, towering above the valley below, and whispered: 'You're right. Love is the only way; it's the only chance of wresting the world out of the hands of Satan. But how are people to know that it's worth taking the risk, that it's worth abandoning the ways of the world? You need to do something that will convince them. You remember what it says in the psalms: "He will put his angels in charge of you... they will bear you up in their hands lest you strike your foot against a stone." People need a sign. Throw yourself down from here, and God, true to his promise, will rescue you. You'd be quite a celebrity; everyone would be impressed; they'd believe you – and they'd love you!'

Jesus did lots of impressive things, curing all manner of diseases, casting out demons, even calming a storm, but he never sought to publicise what he did or to use his deeds as though they were his credentials. Often he told people to keep what had happened to them to themselves, and not to publicise it. He didn't want people to be impressed by the wonders he performed, but to look beyond them to where they pointed – to God, who alone was the author of what Jesus did. Using the gifts of God to point to oneself – behaving just like a celebrity – is to misuse those gifts. Celebrity attracts attention to itself; there's nothing beyond it; no depth, no meaning. The love that it generates has no depth, it's just superficial. And celebrity always has to prove itself; there is a constant challenge to become more and more impressive, spectacular or outrageous. The demon was actually tempting Jesus to challenge God to prove himself, to put God to the test. Jesus' final rebuke summed up the demon's whole approach, and silenced him: 'You shall not put the Lord your God to the test.'

IT took us a long time to learn and take to heart what Jesus had learnt in the wilderness about God's way of being the Messiah. Being a servant seemed pretty tame; that's not the way to get things done, we said. But Jesus taught us to ask ourselves what our ultimate purpose was: if it's giving people new life and new hope then the ways of the world don't work. But those ways are always there, constant temptations to take the wrong path. As he warned us, the devil never gives up; he just bides his time.

7
FOLLOW ME

Mark 1.14-45; 2.13-14; Luke 5.1-11

After his time in the Judean wilderness, Jesus returned to Galilee where he began his ministry proclaiming the gospel of God. Mark summarises his proclamation in these words:

> The time has come; the kingdom of God is upon you.
> Repent and believe the gospel.   *Mark 1.15*

*Apart from this, Mark gives no details of Jesus' first Galilean journey, but Luke does. He says that Jesus went from Capernaum to Nazareth teaching and healing; he then returned to Capernaum where he taught in the Synagogue and met Simon, whose mother-in-law he healed of a high fever. Sometime later, walking along the shore of the lake at Capernaum, he saw Simon again and some of the other fishermen; the encounter changed their lives. Simon's brother **Andrew** was one of them.*

CATCHING fish is what I know about. Most of the men in Capernaum are fishermen, just like their fathers before them. My brother Simon, and old Zebedee's sons, James and John – actually all the men we know – work on the lake. It's hard work, but we make a living. Simon and I expected that we'd always be fishermen, but that's not how it worked out. One day our lives were turned upside-down.

It was when Jesus, the prophet from Nazareth, came to Capernaum. He'd been before. Simon had met him – Jesus had been to his house – but I'd been unwell with a fever that was going around and I missed him. Ever since, Simon and the others had talked of little else: what Jesus had said and done, the cures he'd performed, and especially the authority with which he spoke. He'd healed Simon's mother-in-law, who had the same fever as me. They'd been really worried about her, but Jesus went to her bedside, took hold of her hand and raised her to her feet. The fever left her immediately!

I was so disappointed to miss Jesus; I seemed to be missing all the excitement. Not so long ago everyone had been talking about a man called John who had been baptising in the Jordan. If he hadn't been so far away I expect we would have gone. He said we must prepare for God's new beginning. Well, we were ready for something new; no wonder everyone had been flocking to John!

We'd had enough of the Romans. They held our religion and our customs in contempt, and we were fed up with the way our own leaders, the chief priests and the scribes, kow-towed to them and didn't stand up for us. We tried to be good Jews; we believed in God and said our prayers; we looked after those in need, as it says in the scriptures; but it's hard – impossible if you're a fisherman – to keep all the religious rules: you'd never catch any fish! The Pharisees and the other pious people looked down on us. They thought we were beyond the pale! It didn't seem to occur to them that if no one got their hands dirty there'd be no food on their tables. I heard that John had said that he was preparing the way for the Lord; some thought he was the Messiah, but he said, 'No.' There was One coming who was mightier than him. And now lots of people were saying that One was Jesus. That's why we all wanted to see him.

One day, when we'd worked all night and had caught nothing, Simon and me and James and John were talking about all this – about God, about our hopes for the Messiah, about why religion had to be so complicated. 'It can't have started out like this,' I said, 'why can't we get back to what it's really about. If Jesus comes to Capernaum again, I want to know what he'd say.' And the others agreed. While we were talking we heard voices, it sounded like a crowd coming our way They came from every direction, running down the streets and alleys, crowding along the shore and on to the beach. This could only mean one thing: Jesus *was* coming to the lakeside. When he arrived there were so many people there was nowhere for him to stand. Recognising Simon, he climbed into our boat and asked us to put out a little from the shore. And for an hour or more everyone listened spellbound. I was sitting at the feet of Jesus; this was what I'd been longing for!

When he'd finished he asked Simon to put out into deep water and let down the nets for a catch. It seemed pointless to us. We'd worked all night and caught nothing, but we did as he said. Very quickly the net grew heavy. We couldn't believe it; the net was filled to bursting! It was such a huge catch that we shouted to James and John to come and help us. Any more and both boats would have capsized. Delight and amazement turned to awe: Who was this man? Who were we to receive such blessing? We were overwhelmed, unworthy, afraid in the presence of such goodness. Simon spoke for us all as he fell to his knees in front of Jesus: 'Go, Lord,' he said, 'leave me, sinner that I am.' Jesus looked at us with eyes that saw right into your soul and said, 'Do not be afraid. Come, follow me, and I will make you fishers of men.'

And that's what we did. That's how it all began. Old Zebedee and the hired men looked on amazed as we brought the boats to land, left them to deal with the huge catch, folded our nets and followed him. The net bursting with fish was a sign that spoke to us more loudly than any words. Jesus was someone you could trust. 'Fishers of men' sounded good, but we didn't really take it in; and if we had, we certainly would not have understood what he meant. All we knew was that something about him just connected with all our hopes and feelings. He was the way. It didn't feel as though we had a choice.

BEING with him was almost overwhelming. When we went with him to the synagogue he was invited to speak, and, as usual, everyone was amazed at the authority with which he spoke. What he said connected with ordinary life. He taught that God was like a loving father – we'd thought he was more like a demanding overlord, what with all the rules and regs we were meant to keep. Jesus showed the love of God as he cast out unclean spirits and healed those who were ill.

As he was speaking, suddenly there was a scream. Everyone looked round. There was a man standing up – there was something strange about him – and he shrieked at Jesus: 'What do you want with us, Jesus of Nazareth? Have you come to destroy us? I know who you are – the Holy One of God.' We were shocked, and more than a bit scared. This wasn't what normally happened in the synagogue! But Jesus realised that the man had an unclean spirit, and immediately ordered it to come out of the man. He was thrown into convulsions, fell to the ground and let out a loud cry. The unclean spirit had been overcome. The man was healed.

Everyone was amazed; it was impossible for the service to continue after this as everyone began to talk excitedly. 'What is this?' they exclaimed. 'We've never seen anything like it! He teaches with authority and even the unclean spirits obey him.'

Stories of his cures spread like wild-fire, and people flocked to him – it seemed like the whole town was there. There was one very moving occasion when a leper knelt before him and begged him for help. I've seen lots of lepers, but this man was in a bad way, awfully disfigured. He managed to kneel unaided – no one dared touch a leper for fear of contagion. He pleaded with Jesus: 'If only you will, you can make me clean.'

Jesus stretched out his hand and touched him – we caught our breath in horror – and said, 'I will; be clean.' And immediately the leprosy left him. We were tough men, but there were tears in our eyes.

Jesus wouldn't hang around; there was a great urgency about him. He never stayed long in the same place, even though people kept seeking him out. Within a few days of meeting him we set off on a journey throughout Galilee. His message was actually more important to him than the healing. Later, we grasped that his healing powers pointed to the truth of his teaching, they were a sign of who he was. What he came to do was to proclaim his gospel, his 'good news'. He kept on saying 'Let us move on so that I can proclaim my message in the neighbouring towns as well, for that is what I came to do.'

Lots of his cures were done on the Sabbath. We were shocked for sure, but the Pharisees were appalled! Healing was work, and work was not allowed on the Sabbath. It wasn't long before this reached the ears of the chief priests and the scribes. They wanted to put an end to it, and conflict soon became part of our life. We began to sense the threat very early on. As his fame grew, so did the determination of the authorities to bring him to heel, but they were frustrated through fear of the people who clearly believed, like we did, that God was with him.

They were appalled by the company that Jesus kept: he ate with tax collectors and sinners! He even called one tax-man, Levi, to be one of his followers, like us. We didn't like that; Levi was a collaborator, raising money for the Romans. But Jesus said he came to call the lost, the sinners – reaching out to the lost sheep of the House of Israel is how he described it – and if we were with him we had to look on them as God did. This was a challenge, all right! And the longer we were with him the more the challenges grew: to accepted customs and ideas, to our ways of thinking about God, to the religious rules and rituals, to the authority of the priests.

Gradually it became clear to us that Jesus thought of himself as something more than a prophet; quite what we weren't sure. He referred to himself ambiguously as the 'Son of Man', and claimed authority over the religious laws. It happened one sabbath when we were walking through the fields. Jesus plucked some wheat to eat – not a big deal, you might think, but you'd be wrong. Plucking wheat is work. When challenged by the Pharisees (they were never far away) he replied, 'The sabbath was made for man, not man for the sabbath: so the Son of Man is lord even of the sabbath.' He couldn't have made his challenge more direct!

I WAS beginning to feel very vulnerable, and I wasn't the only one. I talked about it with Simon. He reminded me of what we'd been saying just before we met Jesus: how we were fed up with the way things were, with the chief priests and all the religious rules. 'Yes,' I said, 'but I'd no idea that changing things would be so demanding personally. Have you noticed how some people avoid us when they find out that we're with Jesus?'

It was true. Jesus was compelling, but also very disturbing, and people were dividing into two groups: for him and against him. It wasn't just the authorities who were against him, but all sorts of ordinary folk who just wanted a quiet life. I guess we all want things to change so long as we don't have to change, but we were beginning to realise that this was not possible. It wasn't long before we also began to realise that the authorities had him in their sights. Anyone could see they couldn't remain passive in the face of such a direct challenge to the law. We began to be anxious about ourselves; how long would it be before we too were in their sights?

8
MURMURING

Mark 2.1 –3.19a

As Andrew said, from the beginning of his ministry Jesus attracted hostility from the religious establishment. Reports about Jesus reached the chief priests in Jerusalem, in particular that his teaching departed from the religious law, or Torah. Mark says that scribes came down from Jerusalem to find out what Jesus was doing. One of them, **Ehud,** an official of the Sanhedrin, the highest religious court, wrote a report for the High Priest (he refers to Jesus by his Hebrew name).

From Ehud, Scribe & Servant to the Sanhedrin
To the Most Excellent Caiaphas, High Priest of Israel

Your Excellency,

Blessings and peace be to you! Out of your concern for the People and their salvation, conscious of your sacred duty to uphold Torah and our Traditions, and alarmed by reports that Joshua-bar-Joseph, an unlearned carpenter from Nazareth, was teaching the people contrary to Torah and Tradition, you sent me to Galilee to enquire whether what had been reported to you was true.

I have made careful enquiry and personal observation, and I have to tell your Excellency that the reports are true, and that there is much else about this man that, unless it is checked, will disturb the peace and undermine established order. But such is his popularity and natural authority, that whatever action is taken will have to be carefully devised if it is not to rebound upon us by causing a disturbance that attracts the Governor's attention. Joshua-bar-Joseph is not like the other trouble-makers with whom we have had to deal, as your Excellency will see from my report.

TEACHING

Joshua-bar-Joseph is best described as an itinerant teacher and healer. Some even regard him as a prophet. He is called 'Rabbi' even though he has no learning or status. By the time of my visit he had travelled all over Galilee and had spoken in many synagogues. He has a very large following and can attract crowds of many hundreds wherever he goes. His message is unashamedly populist. He consorts with tax-collectors and sinners; when challenged he replies, 'It is not the healthy that need a doctor but the sick. I did not come to call the virtuous, but sinners.' Although uneducated, he is well grounded in the scriptures; his teaching seems to be based more on the prophets than on the Law, and presents a radically different approach to accepted teaching. He sits light to tradition and does not observe the customary fasts. When challenged about this he said: 'Can you expect the bride-groom's friends to fast while the bridegroom is with them? As long as he is with them there can be no fasting.'

Identifying himself with the Bridegroom, that is with the LORD,* is both blasphemous and inflammatory; it also makes clear that he thinks of himself as having a God-given mission. He refers to himself by the Danielic title 'Son of Man,' and does not distance himself from its Messianic associations; indeed he encourages that association. One sabbath he and his disciples plucked some ears of corn to eat as they were walking though a field. When some Pharisees challenged him over this breach of the sabbath, he likened it to the time when King David and his men ate the sacred bread when Abiathar was High Priest, saying, 'The sabbath was made for man, not man for the sabbath: so the Son of Man is lord even of the sabbath.' Clearly, he is intent on subverting both the Law and priestly authority.

HEALING

The same claims, and the same blasphemy, underlie his healings. This may be our area of greatest difficulty because there is no doubt that Joshua-bar-Joseph has remarkable powers of healing (the like of which I have not seen before), and this is a major part of his appeal. People go to great lengths to bring the sick to him, and no one is turned away. On one occasion four men brought their friend who was paralysed. Because they could not get near to Jesus, they made an opening in the roof at the house where he was teaching and lowered their friend on his bed through the roof! On another occasion I saw him heal a man with a withered arm. In both cases the healing was accomplished by a simple word of command – no touching or anointing – and the cure was instantaneous, and, I have to say, astonishing. His authoritative acts are one with his authoritative words. But both also give cause for serious alarm. One man was healed on the sabbath in open defiance of the Law, but Joshua-bar-Joseph prepared the way very cleverly. He tried to trap us by asking if it was permitted to do good or evil on the sabbath, 'to save life or to kill?' Of course, we kept silent. This angered him, and then he commanded the man to stretch out his arm, and as he did so he was healed.

We have to take a most serious view of disobedience to the sabbath laws, but more serious still is his blasphemy. When he healed the paralysed man brought by his four friends he claimed the power to forgive sins! I wanted to cover my ears as he said to the man, 'My son, your sins are forgiven.' We were speechless. No one apart from God can forgive sins. He guessed what we were thinking, and shamefacedly tried to put us in the wrong by asking why we were harbouring such thoughts! He then said: 'But to convince you that the Son of Man has authority on earth to forgive sins' – he turned to the paralysed man – 'I say to you, stand up, take your bed, and go home.' Everyone, even the scribes, was astounded: 'Never before', they said, ' have we seen anything like this.' And that, in a nutshell, your Excellency, is the basis both of his popularity and of our problem: it is widely believed that he has been sent by God.

FOLLOWERS

Joshua-bar-Joseph has a very large following, attracting crowds of many hundreds wherever he goes. As part of his populist appeal, he makes a point of befriending people who are unclean, who lead immoral lives, and who are social outcasts, like tax-collectors. In villages and small towns the whole population will gather to hear him and bring the sick for healing. He appeals to everyone, high and low, rich and poor, men and women; and he has support even among the Pharisees and educated people. Some make long journeys, coming not just from Galilee but also from Tyre and Sidon, Judea and Jerusalem, Idumaea and Transjordan – Gentiles are treated by Jesus as the same as Jews. Clearly this level of popular support could be used to mount a serious challenge to the authority of the Sanhedrin, although, no doubt, much of his support would not remain firm if he did mount such a challenge.

However, the signs are that he plans to do so. On one occasion in north Galilee, he chose from his followers an inner group, and they now accompany him; they are provided for by a number of women who clearly have the resources to do so. This inner group are a strange mix, with no common ideology or interest. Most are simple fishermen or artisans, one is a former tax-collector (a wretched man called Levi), another a member of the local Zealot party; the only one with any education is a man called Judas Iscariot with whom I spoke briefly. My instincts tell me that he may be useful to us, so I have asked one of our men to keep discreetly in contact. Although this group are an odd collection, the very act of appointing an inner group is a clear sign that he is founding a movement, and the fact that they number twelve discloses his intentions: Israel is a Chosen People of twelve tribes; Joshua-bar-Joseph clearly intends to found a new Israel.

ASSESSMENT

There is no doubt in my mind that Joshua-bar-Joseph is a subversive blasphemer who believes himself to be the Messiah. His popularity means that we must act carefully. He must be eliminated, but at a time of our choosing; in the meantime he must be opposed and some of our people should be briefed to expose him as a blasphemer. This will go some way to undermining his popular support.

While he is in Galilee we cannot move against him as he is in King Herod's jurisdiction, and the king, as your Excellency is only too aware, is not sympathetic to us. I think it is unlikely that Herod will try to take action himself, as he believes that Joshua-bar-Joseph is John the Baptiser, whom he executed, brought back to life. Others may try – I heard reports that some local Pharisees were plotting with men of Herod's party to bring about his death – but I do not think they will succeed. The logic of Joshua-bar-Joseph's message and self-understanding is that he must come to Jerusalem where we shall be able to take action against him. It is important that the Governor, Pontius Pilate, understands our position, and I would advise your Excellency to begin work immediately on an approach that will get him on our side.

9
WHO IS MY MOTHER?

Mark 3.19b-35; Luke 2.22-38

Jesus had more admirers than followers; more sought healing than believed his message. Most people remained apart, his family among them. Mark says they thought he was 'out of his mind.' Relationships in families can be difficult, particularly when one member takes an unexpected path, and this seems to have been the case with Jesus. Although Luke says Mary treasured in her heart the angel's message that he would be son of the Most High, it seems she didn't really understand what Jesus was about, because later she and the rest of the family, believing that he was out of his mind, tried to take him in hand. **Hannah**, *one of Jesus' sisters, explains how they felt:*

WE weren't a large family, but large or small, all families have certain expectations of the eldest son. One day he will be the head of the family. If the family has a business, like we do, he will have to take it over and see that our mother and the younger ones are provided for.

When our parents married, our father, Joseph, was much older than our mother. He died when I was nine; Jesus must have been about twenty-one, and he and my brothers continued the family business. We thought it odd that Jesus did not marry, as my other brothers did, but I was glad to have him at home.

Mother worried about him. He had a restless spirit, and she sensed there was something inside him taking him away from us. Of all her children, I was the closest to her. One day she confided that just after he was born, when they took him to the Temple for her purification, an old man met them – I think she said his name was Simeon. He took Jesus in his arms and prophesied that he was the One destined to restore Israel to glory, but he would be a sign that would be rejected. He said because of him, mother would be pierced to the heart. Many in Israel would stand or fall because of him; he would expose the secret thoughts of their hearts. And that wasn't all. There was a very old lady called Anna (one of the 'temple widows', as we call them, who spend all their time in the Temple praying) – this lady came up to them and gave thanks to God that she had seen the one who was to bring liberation to Jerusalem.

She and Joseph were so astonished that they hadn't known what to make of it at the time – perhaps they were just a couple of Temple cranks – and eventually they forgot about it. But recently the change mother had noticed in Jesus brought back the old man's words, and her anxieties were confirmed when he said he was going to leave the family business in the hands of James, the next eldest, and go to Judea where our cousin John – another one who left his family – was preaching. At the time, apparently, lots of people were talking about over-throwing the Romans – the Zealot Party had just been formed. Mother feared that Jesus was going to join the Zealots and train as a freedom fighter.

We were devastated; family and kinship are ties that cannot be broken; they bring obligations. How would we cope? What would everyone in Nazareth think? We tried to dissuade him, but it was no use. Mother was right, something inside him was driving him away, and he left us.

We had no idea when we would see him again, but after two months or so he returned. He hadn't joined the Zealots; he was still the brother we remembered, but something had changed him – or rather, his inner spirit that mother had sensed, was now plain for all to see. He had become a healer and a teacher, and it wasn't long before stories about him began to reach us – extraordinary stories about miraculous healings and exorcisms, and of crowds of people who were astounded at the authority with which he spoke.

It was his teaching that brought us a new anxiety. He might not have chosen the way of violence, but lots of people found him a disruptive presence. He challenged the way things were; he offended the scribes and the Pharisees; he kept bad company – one of his followers was a former tax-gatherer; he didn't observe the customary fasts; and, worst of all, he worked on the Sabbath and even claimed he had the power to forgive sins! The priests were incensed. If he went on like this he'd soon be arrested and executed as a blasphemer. We could see it coming!

So could the authorities. One day we heard that some scribes had been sent from Jerusalem to see what was going on – actually, I think they had more or less made up their minds. It was common knowledge they thought he was possessed by a devil, and it was by the power of Satan that he was performing his cures. I didn't know what to make of it, but the idea of him being in league with Satan seemed absurd. Satan was the cause of disease and evil spirits; Jesus was hardly going to turn Satan against himself and cast them out!

Well, whatever the truth, the rumour was enough to bring disgrace on the family, and that was too much for our mother, and for James, and for all of us to bear. And it got worse!

Jesus actually insulted the scribes by pointedly showing that their arguments were false. He had no restraint: he accused them of slandering the Holy Spirit, which, he said, was the only unforgivable sin. We knew what happened to people who did that, who made those in authority lose face. Only those who courted disaster, or who were out of their mind did that! He must have gone over the edge. We had to protect him and take charge of him for his own good. Mother and my brothers set out to find him.

But worse was to come. When they arrived at the house where he was, he refused to see them. There was nothing they could do. He was surrounded by his followers, and just as pointedly as he had spoken to the scribes, he now spoke to them, his own family. 'Who are my mother and my brothers?' he asked. And then, looking at those gathered around him he said, 'Here are my mother and my brothers. Whoever who does the will of God is my brother and sister and mother.'

Some said his vision of heaven was like an inclusive family. It didn't feel like that to us; we felt utterly rejected. We were no longer his family. It was awful. Who were these people who had taken our brother away?

10

IF YOU HAVE EARS TO HEAR

Mark 4.1-34

*Jesus' family may have thought he was out of his mind, but many did not, and his teaching spoke to them. He used everyday situations to paint pictures of God and his goodness. On one occasion he spoke about seeds: the good and bad fortune that follows sowing; the way they are transformed as they grow, we know not how; and the wonder of so much coming out of so little. Listening to Jesus could be a transforming encounter, but his message was deeply challenging, not just to the priests and the scribes but also to the prevailing social and economic order. He taught that under the kingly rule of God things will be ordered differently to the way they are ordered by men. As they listened, many felt their basic assumptions were being undermined. **Jethro**, a farmer, had this experience as he listened to Jesus among the crowd at the lakeside.*

YES, I was there. I'd heard about Jesus of Nazareth from Mahli, a friend who had been in the crowd outside the house in Capernaum – you know, the one where they tore off the roof and lowered a crippled man in front of Jesus. Mahli has never stopped talking about it, so when I heard that Jesus was in Capernaum again I went along. I wanted to hear him for myself, and I hoped I'd see him perform a miracle.

There was a huge crowd gathered on the shore, so many that he had to climb into a boat so that we could all see him. And then he spoke – and it's true what they say, this man holds your attention; he speaks with authority; you have to listen to him. I'm not one for clever stuff, and nor is Jesus. He used everyday situations to explain what he believed about God, and that made a good deal more sense to me than the stuff you hear in the synagogue.

Our family have been farmers for many generations. Actually 'farmer' gives the wrong impression. Like many people we rent some land from a local landowner and grow our own stuff. We're lucky; we've got a bit more land than most, and so we can sell our surplus. We get by, but life is hard and unfair; the rich get richer, and poor get poorer.

Jesus told a story about a sower that really spoke to those of us who live by the land. We scatter the seed and then plough it in; and because we do it this way it doesn't matter if it falls among weeds, or on the paths, it will all get ploughed in. But you have to reckon with losing quite a bit of seed, and that's what happened in Jesus' story. The farmer sowed his seed, but not all the seed took; some withered for want of good soil, some was choked by weeds, and some was scorched by the sun, but the seed in the good soil produced a harvest beyond all expectations! For me a ten-fold harvest would be very good – we usually get much less than that – but in the story the farmer got thirty-fold, or even sixty-fold, or a hundred-fold! That's way beyond our wildest dreams! How I long for a harvest like that. I could buy my own land and be free!

It was a good story, but at the time I wasn't sure what Jesus meant by it. At the end he said, 'If you have ears to hear, then hear.' For sure, there was more to the story; something was being made clear, like a lamp on a lamp-stand lighting up the house, but what was it?*

The next day I came across Mahli; he'd also been at the lakeside, but I'd missed him. I asked him what he made of it. 'Well,' he said, 'Jesus always talks about God. He likes to paint pictures of how things would be if God's way came on earth as it is in heaven. Heaven on earth would be a harvest where we got thirty-fold, sixty-fold, and more, wouldn't it? If we follow him, and trust in God as he does, then that's how it will be: heaven on earth.'

'OK,' I said, 'but that would be a revolution. If we always got harvests like that we'd be as rich as the landlords. They'd lose their power and status – and so would the priests. Is that what he wants?'

'Yes. Something like that, but not violent revolution. I don't think revolution ever fulfils the original hopes; it just replaces one set of oppressors with another. I think Jesus is after some-thing different: a deep and lasting change in the way we do things, particularly in our ideas of justice. You remember what he said about the seed growing secretly? God brings about the change that transforms the seed into the plant, but it takes time. Trust in God and he will make all things new.

'You know, Jethro, Jesus reminds me of Isaiah. He condemned the corruption in Israel and said God wanted to establish justice and protect the vulnerable. You remember the passage: "He will not break a crushed reed or snuff out a smouldering wick; unfailingly he will establish justice…on earth."'

Jethro thought for a moment before replying. 'Yes, vaguely. So you think that's what he's about. "Follow me, and things will change. God will do a new thing, and you will have the kind of joy that comes with an abundant harvest. It will exceed your wildest dreams!"'

'Exactly. Just like Isaiah.'

'But that's powerful stuff, Mahli. No wonder the priests and the scribes are wary of him! Do you remember the look on his face when he spoke about the measure you get? "Take note of what you hear," he said, "those who have will be given more and those who have not will forfeit even what they have." You know, I took him literally: that's the way it is in the world. But that look was meaningful; I think what he actually meant was:

"This is how it may be in the world, but not how it shall be in God's kingdom."'

'Yes, Jethro, I think you're right. That's his vision; that's what he's about. But have we got the courage for it? Who knows where it would lead. Life may be hard and unfair, but at least we know where we are. Do we really want all the upheaval that the kingdom would bring?'

MAHLI'S words weighed with me. I'm not sure I want to be uprooted from the life I know, even if it brought me freedom. But on my way home I thought about the last of Jesus' stories – the one about the mustard tree. He used it as a picture of what life would be like under God's kingly rule: from the smallest of seeds grows a tree big enough for the birds to roost in its shade. I have a mustard tree. When I planted it the seed was so small I wondered if it would germinate. It did, and it never ceases to amaze me that so much can come out of such a small beginning. That, said Jesus, is how it is with God. If you have ears to hear, then hear.

11

YOUR FAITH HAS CURED YOU

Mark 5.21-6.6a

When Jethro went to the lakeside what he really wanted was to see a miracle. He was disappointed, but crowds of people did witness these mighty acts. Many must have come to Jesus out of a need for healing, others came simply to see wonders performed in front of their eyes, and some just happened to be there. Everyone saw the same acts and heard the same words, but some saw beyond the wonder; for them Jesus' miracles were a sign of his divinity and an encounter with the power of God. One of those was Michal, a woman whom Jesus healed of haemorrhages. Today, we tend to miss an important aspect of the story, because we're accustomed to the idea of men and women being equal, even if that's not how it always is in practice. In Jesus' day, women, along with children, were very much second-class in status, so the way that Jesus reached out to Michal was all the more remarkable. Michal's friend, **Ruth**, tells what happened.*

THE day began as always, getting water, sweeping the house, and preparing the food. Usually I take my time, but on that day I hurried. The news was spreading like wildfire that the prophet Jesus had come back across the lake, and everyone was going to the shore. I'd heard about him calming the storm on the lake and the pigs rushing into the sea – as you can imagine, it was the talk of the town! Clearly he had amazing powers – I had to see him for myself. I was excited, but I was also a bit scared!

As I left the house I saw my friend, Michal, and walked with her. Her health was bad. For twelve years she had suffered from haemorrhages. She'd been to see so many doctors that she'd lost count, and was in despair. They'd all said they could cure her, but none of them did. They were all worse than useless! And she'd spent a lot of money on them – not that she had much in the first place, but it had all gone, and now she was poor as well as sick, and getting worse.

She'd heard of the cures that Jesus had performed when he was in Capernaum, and she believed he could cure her. He was her last hope. But after all she'd been through she wasn't very confident about approaching him – not like those men who'd torn the roof off to bring their friend to Jesus. She hoped she could get near enough to him just to touch him. She said to me, 'If I touch even his clothes, I shall be healed.' I bit my lip to stop myself crying. Her hope was so strong, and I didn't want her to be disappointed.

When we arrived I managed to get her to the front of the crowd, but already Jairus was pleading with Jesus. Now Jairus is *someone* – president of the synagogue, pretty well top of the tree – but he was on his knees in front of Jesus, begging him to go to his house and lay hands on his daughter who was near to death. She was only twelve years old, born the same year as my friend's trouble started. Seeing Jairus on his knees made you realise how desperate he was! As a person I'd found him a bit distant, but seeing him like that my heart went out to him. Poor man!

As Jesus set off with Jairus to go to his house, Michal managed to go up behind him and touch his cloak. The effect was instantaneous. Jesus stopped in his tracks, turned round and said, 'Who touched my clothes?' We were astonished: how on earth had he sensed it? He spoke gently, but you knew he wanted to know. One of his followers said to him, 'Everybody's touching you. How can you ask, "Who touched me?"' I think they were a bit overawed by Jairus and didn't want to keep him waiting. But Jesus wouldn't move, and looked around to see who had touched him. I could feel Michal trembling with anxiety. She'd been shunned by so many people – they thought her bleeding made her unclean. She just wanted to remain in the shadows, but she couldn't. 'It's alright,' I said, and trembling, she fell down at Jesus' feet and told him what had happened to her: that as soon as she reached out and touched his cloak she knew that the bleeding had stopped. She said to me afterwards that she thought he would rebuke her, but he didn't. He was full of compassion; he knew what she'd been through; how her hope had almost died. He looked at her and he called her 'daughter': 'Daughter,' he said, 'your faith has healed you. Go in peace, free from your affliction.'

We were stunned. It was simply amazing!

And then, one of Jairus' servants came up and said his daughter had died; there was no need to trouble Jesus any more. Jairus turned white. He looked awful; his worst fears realised. He struggled to keep back his tears, but Jesus just said to him: 'Don't be afraid, simply have faith,' and went off to his house. We heard later that when he arrived the people laughed at the idea that he could do anything for the little girl. But he did. He took her hand and said, 'Get up, my child.' And she did! Everyone was awe-struck. Who was this man who could even raise the dead?

WELL, the day may have begun like any other, but it turned out to be a day I'll never forget. The miraculous cures were beyond belief. Bringing the little girl back to life was truly awesome, but so was his awareness that that someone had touched his cloak. Michal's need had drawn power out of him, and he must have felt it. But just as remarkable was the way he reached out to Michal and restored her respectability – even delaying going with an important man like Jairus to attend to a poor woman whom society had rejected. He put the poor before the rich, the lowly before the powerful.

And to cap it all he called her 'Daughter' – I'd never heard anyone say that before, nor had anyone else. You could feel the astonishment: he treated Michal just like a man; she was included not excluded; no one was beyond the pale with God. He says this is how it will be in God's kingdom, and it's not just words with him. He practises what he preaches.

He calls himself the Son of Man; more like the Son of God, I'd say.

After this, Mark says Jesus went to Nazareth, his home town, but the people turned against him. His lack of status was something they could not accept, and they held it against him. For them he was 'the carpenter, the son of Mary, the brother of James and Joses and Judas and Simon.' 'Where does he get it from?' they asked indignantly. 'Who's given him this wisdom? How does he do all these miracles?' When **Ruth** *heard of it, she told Michal what she thought.*

'They must be blind; it's obvious it all comes from God.'

'Well, Ruth, it may be to you and me, but then we didn't grow up with him. I remember feeling the same when my eldest became a Rabbi. He was just my little boy; where did he get it from? We think we know people, don't we? We think we've got them sussed, and we don't want to have to think again. It's just too much of an upheaval to change our minds.

'I guess you're right, though when you're faced with the obvious it does seem pretty stupid not to admit it. But then, if you really listen to Jesus he's turning all sorts of accepted ideas on their heads. I suppose that's why people reject him, even though they've seen what he does. It's crazy – but all too human. Ruth, are you going to become one of his followers?'

Michal's question resonated with Ruth's feelings. She had thought about it, but wasn't sure. She hesitated before replying.

'Well, that puts me on the line! I want to, but not yet. I'm not quite ready. I've got to get used to what it will mean for me. I don't mind re-thinking my ideas about God, but I don't want to be separated from my family and friends. It's a lot to ask.'

'Maybe that's what those people at Nazareth feel – he's asking too much.'

'Yes, maybe that's what it's all about.'

12
ARE YOU THE ONE?

Luke 7.18–35; 8.1–3.

According to Mark news about Jesus spread widely, but, as in Nazareth, not everyone saw his miracles as signs pointing to the truth of who he was. Moreover, Jesus actively discouraged anything like a cult of celebrity. He might well have gained a large following if he had – and that was what Satan had tempted him to do – but it would not have produced true personal faith. And even for those, like Ruth, who did understand the signs, the personal consequences of becoming one of his followers had to be weighed carefully.

Among those who weren't sure about Jesus was John the Baptist, which is surprising given the testimony he bore to him when he was baptised. After the baptism, John was arrested by King Herod Antipas and put in prison (we learn why in the next episode). However, John's disciples reported to him all that Jesus was doing, and John sent them back to Jesus with a basic question. **Ruth** *continues the story:*

MICHAL'S question stayed with me: was I going to follow Jesus? There are several women among those who accompany him – apparently they provide for him and the others out of their own resources. Some are quite well known, like Joanna, Chuza's wife, one of King Herod's stewards, no less. They say she and the other women had been cured by Jesus. Well, I can understand how they feel, and how they want to be close to him – Michal feels the same – but being with him marks you out, and people talk. Having a mixed group of followers, women and men … well, it's asking for trouble; people just don't understand. But then, he speaks with such authority, and what he says seems so right. And treating women like he treats the men seems so right too. Something deep inside me tells me he *is* special, sent from God. I suppose, in my own way, I have become one of his followers. I just have to have the courage to admit it to myself.

I was in the midst of this inner turmoil when I went to see my cousin who lives in a village not far from here. I had become so preoccupied with my thoughts, that I was brought up short when it became apparent that he and his wife didn't know about Jesus. They knew Michal, and I told them about her cure after all those years of illness. They were astonished, alright, but when I said it was Jesus of Nazareth who had cured her, my cousin said, 'Nazareth! You need to be careful associating with people from Nazareth. Nothing good ever came from there!' It was a common prejudice.* I think it wasn't so much that my cousin and his wife had never heard of Jesus, as that they didn't want to know. So I told them the whole story, and it was as I spoke that I realised how much all that Jesus said and stood for meant to me. There I was bearing witness to him from my heart. There could be no more hesitation; I was one of his followers.

On my return I went to see Michal to tell her about my visit and how I felt. She was overjoyed. She had come to the same moment of acceptance, and now we had that in common too. But, she said, some of those who knew Jesus well seemed not to be so sure. 'Like who?' I asked. 'Well, John the Baptiser, would you believe?' That did surprise me.

After her cure, Michal went to listen to Jesus teach as often as she could. On one occasion, some of John's disciples arrived. Jesus recognised them and asked after John who was in prison. They said John had sent them with a question: 'Are you the one who is to come, or are we to expect someone else?' Jesus looked at them in that way he has – it's as though he can see into your soul – and said gently, 'Come and see.' A large crowd had gathered, among them many who were sick, and as he made his way through the crowd Jesus healed all kinds of illnesses, driving out evil spirits, and giving sight to the blind. Afterwards, as the crowd dispersed, he said to John's disciples: 'Tell John what you have seen and heard: the blind regain their sight, the lame walk, lepers are made clean, the deaf hear, the dead are raised to life, the poor are brought good news – and happy is he who does not find me an obstacle to faith.'

'What do you think they made of that?' I asked.

'Well,' Michal replied, 'I've begun to realise that it's typical of Jesus not to give a straight answer. I think he wants us to come to our own conclusions about who he is. There were two scribes there, and I overheard them talking afterwards, and that's what one of them said. They were talking about the messianic signs described by Isaiah – apparently Jesus was quoting Isaiah; I was wondering where I'd heard it before. One of the scribes said Jesus had actually read that passage from Isaiah in the synagogue at Capernaum.'*

'So, Jesus was saying, "You have seen the signs; make up your own mind if I am the one who is to come." I guess John would have got the point.'

'Yes, I think so. That's certainly what the scribes thought. One of them said something that I took to heart. He said faith goes deeper than adulation or admiration. It's a personal commitment, a re-orientation of our life. He's right, Ruth. Faith in Jesus comes from seeing what he does as signs that point to who he really is. We have to be convinced in our own heart that he is the Son of God, and decide to follow his Way.'

I'd come to the same realisation; it's exactly what I'd been saying to my cousin. 'Amen to that!' I said.

13

JOHN THE BAPTIST IS EXECUTED

Mark 6.14-29

John the Baptist was arrested and imprisoned by King Herod Antipas because he had criticised the king for taking Herodias, his brother Philip's wife, and marrying her. Even though John was outspoken, Mark says Herod went in awe of him, 'knowing him to be a good and holy man.' He was reluctant to punish John further and gave him his protection. Queen Herodias felt differently: she 'nursed a grudge against John and would willingly have killed him, but she could not,' so she bided her time. **Shimon,** *one of Herod's servants who had been in attendance when John and Herod had talked together, tells his colleague,* **Dathan,** *who has been away on royal business, about how Herodias took her revenge.*

Dathan, shalom! You're back from Jerusalem. How was it?

Shalom! All went well, but it's good to be home. What's news? How did the king's birthday banquet go? What did I miss?

It's been a hell-of-a-week. I'm all in! And it was some party! What you missed is that the queen finally got her revenge on John the Baptiser. It happened at the banquet.

So, she finally found her chance. Well, it's been no secret that she was just waiting to get even. Abigail, one of her attendants, told me the queen was seething with rage ever since John told the king he had no right to marry his brother's wife. So what happened?

Well, you know how it is with the king, drinking too much, always out to impress... He got the queen's daughter Salome to dance for his guests. Have you seen her dance?

No, but I hear that she's very sensual, wild – and virtually naked.

You can say that again! It was quite a performance! We knew she was good, but this was something else! The king was entranced, and – you know how he loves to make extravagant gestures – he said to Salome, 'Ask me for anything you like and I will give it to you.' He even took an oath, 'Whatever you ask I will give you, up to half my kingdom.'

He said what?

'Up to half my kingdom', more fool him!

I bet Salome hadn't been expecting that.

No she hadn't. She looked bewildered, made an excuse and went out. Apparently she went to the queen – your friend Abigail was in attendance – and asked her what she should ask for. The queen seized her chance: when Salome returned she said to the king: 'I want you to give me, here and now, on a dish, the head of John the Baptist.'

Good God! And the king said yes?

He did, though it sobered him up. His face fell; his distress was plain for all to see. This wasn't what he was expecting; he must have guessed who was behind it, but he gave in and sent one of the guards to behead John. It didn't take long and soon he came back with John's head on a dish and gave it to Salome, who took it to the queen. It was awful!

So, the king's high regard for John wasn't worth much; not compared to his standing in front of the high and mighty.

Absolutely. His vain oath was more important to him than John's life.

You know, Shimon, the king's not just foolish, but weak. He's all swagger and aggression; there's no inner strength. It's all about power and status with these Hasmoneans; justice and right don't get a look in.

Too true. The odd thing is that that is what he talked to John about – justice and right... and God.

Really?

Yes; that's what they talked about. I was there in attendance on the king. Reading between the lines, as it were, I think King Herod wants to feel more Jewish.

Well, coming from Idumea, he's only a half-Jew!

So, he thought John could help him?

Yes, I guess so. They spoke a lot about what makes a person good and acceptable to God.

Goodness me! King Herod's never struck me as having a finer side.

He keeps it well covered! I think that's what all the swagger and aggression is about: covering up his vulnerability. But even he could recognise goodness in John. And then he's superstitious. I think he feared putting a holy man to death.

Well, that's a new line on the king! What else did he talk to John about?

Before John was arrested we'd been getting reports about him, and the king sent a couple of us to check him out. He sounded like the people you read about in the scriptures...

You mean the prophets – like Micah, and Isaiah, and Jeremiah.

Yes, exactly. The king asked John if he was a prophet. He said, 'No.' He was a herald, sent to prepare the way of the Lord, as Isaiah had prophesied: 'A voice cries in the wilderness, "Prepare the way for the Lord; clear a straight path for him."' He told the king he was that voice; he wasn't a prophet, but a herald sent in fulfilment of prophecy.

What did the king make of that?

He looked a bit nonplussed. So were the rest of us. I thought all that Isaiah stuff was in the past; I didn't think it had any relevance to today. And, of course, it was all new to the king.

I can't see prophecy as part of his world view.

No; far from it! He asked John to tell him about Isaiah: When did he live? What did he say? Did John expect his prophecies to be fulfilled?

This is extraordinary!

It was! Well, John didn't need any encouragement to talk about Isaiah. He was John's inspiration. Apparently John's father, Zechariah, was a priest, and the family had expected that John would follow his father. But that wasn't to be. His father had some kind of vision that John had a special destiny – I can't remember all the details – but anyway he felt that all the rules and the rituals, all the stuff that you have to go along with if you're going to be a priest, kept God at a distance. He felt that religion needed freeing from all that. The ordinary people could never keep all the rules; there must be a better way to God.

Well, he's right there! There must be a better way. There are too many rules; you just can't keep them all.

John pointed out to the king that Isaiah had felt much the same, and was unsparing in his criticism of religious ritual. He denounced it all in the name of God. I can hear him now: 'Your countless sacrifices, what are they to me? I have no desire for the blood of bulls... I cannot endure your idolatrous ceremonies... from your prayers I turn away.' *[Isaiah 1.11–15].*

Heavens! Did Isaiah say that? 'From your prayers I turn away.' That's really hard-hitting. So what did he say about justice and right?

That God was on the side of the ordinary people. God wants us, he said, to 'pursue justice, guide the oppressed, uphold the rights of the fatherless and plead the widow's cause.' *[Isaiah 1.17]*

Not exactly Herod's point of view. I'm not surprised he was disturbed.

Actually, you're making me think. I haven't thought much about the prophets. Do they all say the same?

Pretty much. Amos and Micah denounced the rulers of Israel and Judah because of their immorality and oppression, and warned them that the Lord would bring disaster upon them, as he did when they were conquered by Assyria and taken into exile. A tough message for a king!

I suppose John said if they had heeded the prophet's words, the disaster would have been averted.

Precisely. But the king came back to him: 'So, what should they have done?' he asked. John replied, 'The Lord has told you what is good: to act justly, to love loyalty and to walk humbly before him. Let justice flow on like a river and righteousness like a never-failing torrent.'*

What did he make of that?

I think he could see where John was heading and decided he'd had enough. He sent him back to the cells.

But something must have got at him, because he talked to John several times more. I remember John talking about his call to the people to repent. 'What do you mean by repentance?' the king asked. 'Sorting out your inner life; getting yourself right with God,' John replied. 'It's not just being sorry, but a deep desire and determination to change, to turn around, to face another way. It's exactly what the rulers condemned by Amos and Micah refused to do.' The king changed tack.

I bet he did! Let me guess… This was all a long time ago. Times had changed. Rulers like him had to be practical; compromise could not be avoided. Everyone suffers if there's disorder in the land, good and bad alike. It couldn't be risked; the people had to be kept in line.

Yes, you know the script. If necessary you have to use violence. It isn't oppression, just necessity. The end justifies the means.

So, the king had a go at John?

Oh, yes. It wasn't all one way. But John didn't really argue. He just said the prophets didn't see things in that way. God's way, they said, was that good order and prosperity depended on justice, especially justice for the poor. The poor were God's special concern. And that's when he began to talk about the Messiah, and the coming of a new age. You could see that the king wanted to know more, but also that he was scared about what he might hear – after all, the Messiah will be the leader of Israel.

That would have really aroused his insecurity.

Yes, you could see it in his face. And when John began to speak about Micah's prophecy that a ruler would come from Bethlehem to bring justice on earth, and that he believed that we are living in the time when that prophecy has been fulfilled, the king became really agitated, and sent John away. That was the last time they met.

And now John's dead. Killed by his protector. Killed because of a drunken oath. Where was the justice in that? Herod may have listened, but he didn't learn.

They never do.

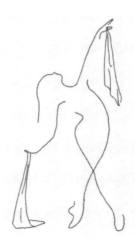

III
Confrontation

Why do you not conform to the ancient tradition? *Mark 7.5*

14

WOE TO YOU!

Mark 6.6b-13; 7.24-37; Luke 11.37-54

Jesus' intentions were peaceful, but even so they were radical: nothing less than calling Israel to a new understanding of both God and the Law by which God's People were to live. It amounted to the re-founding of Israel. His message was entirely in line with that of the prophets, but he took it a step further in calling twelve companions to be with him. The number twelve was significant. Israel was founded with twelve tribes, each one named after one of the sons of the patriarch Jacob, to whom God had given the new name of 'Israel'. The Twelve disciples were to be the nucleus of the New People of God that Jesus' ministry was inaugurating.

At the heart of Jesus' vision was a new way to God through purity of heart and mind, rather than though obedience to the detailed requirements of the law, which most people simply could not observe. This, of course, was a serious challenge to the priests and other religious authorities, as we have seen from the report that the scribe Ehud made to the High Priest. Jesus' basic charge against them was hypocrisy: saying one thing and doing another. His criticisms were biting; Matthew collected some of them in a group of sayings known as the Woes (because that's how they all begin), for example:

> Woe to you, scribes and Pharisees, hypocrites! You pay tithes of mint and dill and cummin; but you have overlooked the weightier demands of the law – justice, mercy and good faith. It is these you should have practised without neglecting the others. Blind guides! You strain off a midge, yet gulp down a camel!
>
> *Matthew 23.23-24*

*Mark does not mention the 'woes', but Luke does; his version is shorter than Matthew's. His setting is a meal to which Jesus was invited by a Pharisee after he had heard him speak. Jesus was outspoken in his criticism of his host and fellow guests (the conventions of dinner-table conversation were evidently quite different in his day). Luke says only that Jesus was invited, but clearly there were other guests because what Jesus said to his host became common knowledge. It is likely that some of the disciples were among the other guests. One of them, **Thaddaeus**, tells what happened and what it meant to him to be sent out by Jesus to preach and to heal in his name.*

AT first being with Jesus was like being in our own private school. He was constantly on the move, but as we walked, and in the evenings as we ate together, he would teach us. We also learned a lot from what Jesus did, especially the way he reached out over barriers. We'd all been brought up to regard those who weren't Jews and lived by different customs, as beyond the pale, and to keep ourselves separate from them. But Jesus wasn't like that. Once, when we were near Tyre, a local woman, a Phoenician from Syria, begged him to drive out the unclean spirit that was possessing her daughter. At first, we thought he was going to refuse – he said it wasn't right to take the children's bread and throw it to the dogs. It sounds harsh, but it wasn't harshly said, and there was an ironic look in his face as he spoke. The woman responded in kind: 'Sir, even the dogs under the table eat the children's scraps.' He was just testing her faith, and when she went home she found her daughter healed. We learnt that with Jesus there were no barriers to his friendship.

He made it clear that we were to have the same attitude, to proclaim the same message, and to do the same work as him. He couldn't go everywhere, and he spoke about sending us out in pairs to the villages he did not visit himself. Well, we were all pretty apprehensive at the prospect! None of us had his gift with words, his natural authority, nor his knowledge of the scriptures. He was aware of our anxiety; all he said was, 'Don't be afraid. I will be with you in spirit; the words will come. Have faith.'

He wasn't one to hang about. I think we'd only been with him five or six months, when the time came. One evening, after supper, he called us together and said that the next day he was going to send us out in pairs. We were to proclaim the 'Good News', and we were to trust the local people to provide what we needed. 'Take nothing for the journey,' he said, 'except a staff. No food, no clothes, no money.' Then we all knelt while he prayed. He asked God to go with us, to place his words in our hearts and on our lips, and then he stretched out his hands over us and said, 'I give you my authority to heal the sick and to drive out all unclean spirits.'

It was always special when Jesus prayed; a deep sense of connection with God. There were many such moments, but that was one I will never forget. My spirit stirred within me as never before; I felt a new sense of confidence and power. It was like the healing he performed on a man in the Decapolis. He was deaf and could not speak clearly. Jesus opened his ears and freed his tongue with the command, 'Ephphatha' – 'Be opened.' When we could hear clearly the word of God in our hearts, we'd know what to say. Intuitively, I felt that clarity.

And so the next day we went out, and it was as Jesus had said. We anointed the sick and healed them, and drove out many evil spirits. And the people responded to our message – and to us, after all, we were humble folk like them. Our deeds of healing gave authority to our words: that God was love and promised forgiveness to all who truly repented. I was amazed, and humbled. Actually, to be used in that way was the most humbling experience of my life. And I felt a new person, more confident as a companion of Jesus. I wasn't one of the inner group, like Peter, James and John, or even like Andrew and Philip, but I had received the same gift as them, and I had been used in the same way. It was so affirming, and my heart overflowed with thanks.

The contrast between the way the ordinary people responded to Jesus and the Pharisees was very evident. They came to hear what he said, but they couldn't accept his teaching so readily; they wanted to fit it in to their tradition. I remember one Pharisee called Shimon. Frequently he came to listen to Jesus and on one occasion invited him to a meal afterwards. It often happened, and some of us might also be invited. On that occasion a few of us were talking to Jesus when Shimon approached him, and he invited us too. We were scarcely in the door when our host remarked with surprise that Jesus did not wash his hands before eating.

This was the kind of petty rule with which Jesus had no patience. It was all about what people did outwardly rather than where their hearts were inwardly. His response was very pointed. Looking straight at Shimon he said, 'You Pharisees clean the outside of cup and plate; but inside you are full of greed and wickedness. You fools! Did not God, who made the outside, also make the inside? But give what is in your cups to the poor, and everything will be clean for you.' Shimon and the others were quite taken aback. But that wasn't all. He took them to task for the way they meticulously measured out tithes, even of garden herbs, but neglected the weightier demands of justice and the love of God. Their love of status – having the best seats in the synagogue and being greeted respectfully in the street – led them astray. They were blind guides.

This was too much for another of the guests, a lawyer, who protested that Jesus was insulting them too. Clearly Jesus' words had struck home, but he intended no insult. For those buoyed up with self-regard, the truth can feel like an insult, but what Jesus wanted was to bring about repentance. It's what he did all the time: he held up a mirror so that people could see what they were really like, and make amends. He came back directly to the lawyer: 'Alas for you lawyers also! You load men with intolerable burdens, and will not lift a finger to lighten the load.' Not only had they not taken to heart the message of the prophets (who had said exactly the same as Jesus),* they had taken away the key of knowledge so no one could find out for themselves.

Some of us found Jesus' attitude alarming. What he said was true – double standards were everywhere – having a true spirit was more important than observing the petty rules – but these pointed attacks were just building up opposition. After that dinner the way he was hounded by the lawyers and the Pharisees got a lot worse. What they wanted to do was to undermine his popularity by catching him with his own words.

They'd have a hard job because he had right on his side. Not only that, but the picture of God that he painted was just so different to the demanding, awesome picture of the priests and the lawyers. His 'woes' were pronounced over those with narrow, legalistic, elitist attitudes. In contrast, he said the Kingdom was a wide fellowship; the way to it might be hard, but that wasn't because it was strewn with rules, but because it required a purity and generosity of heart that took time to acquire. What really made him angry was the hardness of heart so often shown by those with wealth, status and power. There are some people who will never be convinced, who just won't look in the mirror. When he sent us out he had warned us that some would refuse to listen. If they don't receive you, he said, shake the dust off your feet as you leave, as a solemn warning. We were learning it is our response to Jesus that determines our destiny.

15

You pay me lip-service

Mark 4.35–5.20; 7.1–23.

Many of Jesus' encounters were confrontational, and throughout his ministry he engaged in a running dispute with the religious establishment: the priests, the scribes and the Pharisees. They followed him around, even making the long journey from Jerusalem to Galilee, as we saw in episode 8. They were a constant, hostile presence.

Jesus was particularly critical of the way the Torah (the basic Law of Moses contained in the first five books of the Bible) had been elaborated by the scribes and the priests. Mark gives two examples: the food laws and the practice of corban. 'Corban' means a sacrificial offering as described by the Torah. Originally these were offerings of animals or grain, but came to include financial offerings. By the time of Jesus, some Jews were avoiding their responsibility to their parents by designating some of their financial resources as 'corban', thus preventing them from being used for supporting parents and family. The food laws were designed to avoid ritual uncleanliness, and covered matters like the slaughter of animals, which meats could be eaten, the use of vessels in cooking, and the washing of hands before meals.

It was over this last matter that a group of scribes and Pharisees took Jesus to task: 'Why do your disciples not conform to the ancient tradition, but eat their food with defiled hands?' they demanded. And Jesus, in reply, accuses them of hypocrisy, quoting Isaiah's condemnation that they paid only lip-service to God; their hearts were far from him. They taught as divine law the commandments of men.

*This was stinging criticism, but, even so, not all of them were against him. Many Pharisees sympathised with Jesus, and some of them even became disciples. Even within the establishment there was disagreement about who Jesus was. After a second visit to Galilee two Pharisees, **Nathaniel** and **Omri**, argued it out. Nathaniel, the less sympathetic of the two, begins:*

Well, Omri, he hasn't changed his tune. It's just like it was when we came before; if anything he's sharpened up his attacks. What do you make of it?

Well, yes – it's got worse. But he does do some remarkable things. You remember we heard from Judas how he calmed a storm? And his healings are astonishing. Apparently in the Decapolis he healed a man who was both deaf and dumb! That, as you know, is one of the messianic signs.* He may sit light to the law, but I find it hard to say he's doing Satan's work.

I'm not accusing him of that.

Well, some do. Like the group who said he was possessed by Beelzebul, and drove out demons by his power. [Cf. Mark 3.22]

That was a group of mischievous scribes, and, I have to say, I was pleased when he put them in their place! But his powers are not unique. There have been rabbis before him, like Honi, who could affect the weather and perform remarkable healings.*

But left to himself he's becoming a menace. You heard about the pigs – his exorcism of Legion, and the way he sent the unclean spirits into a herd of pigs who all rushed into the sea and perished? I know they were pigs and unclean, but killing a whole herd... What on earth did he think he was doing?

Heaven knows! I find that very disturbing; I really don't know what to make of it. At the least it brought order to a severely disturbed man, and we should be thankful for that. But I'm not surprised that the people begged him to go away.

Nor am I! But this is not the real point. We've had healers and miracle-workers before and we'll have them again, I don't doubt, but they haven't attacked our Law and traditions as he does, like the way he declared all foods clean, and undermined our practice of corban. In my view this puts him into a different category; he is a dangerous subversive.

Well, actually, I agree with him about corban. He made me realise that we do use it to evade the fifth commandment. It had never occurred to me before – he opened my eyes.

Is he subversive? I don't think so. It's not that he sits light to the Law; he challenges our interpretation. And we're not used to that, and so far our response hasn't been very convincing. The trouble is he has scripture on his side.

What on earth do you mean? We use corban to glorify God – there's nothing in scripture that forbids that! And the food laws are part of the Torah; you can't get more scriptural than that!

True – to a point. The foundation may be Torah, but the rules have been endlessly elaborated.

They needed to be! Ordinary people need detailed guidance for all eventualities.

That's very pharisaic! Actually, I was thinking about Isaiah. He condemned Israel for paying lip-service to God, as Jesus said. Didn't Isaiah say we worshipped God with empty words, paying him lip-service while our hearts are far away? Religion had become a human precept, learnt by rote? He said God would shock us out of our complacency. Sometimes I wonder if Jesus is that shock.*

What's shocking is that he's trying to undermine our credibility! Clearly, Omri, you haven't grasped the situation properly. Isaiah was a great prophet, but his words are not Torah. Torah is our foundation. It defines who we are; it gives us our identity. We are the People set apart for God – that's what these rules are about. Abandon the Law and who are we?

Nothing; no better than the rest: Romans, Egyptians, Syrians –
you name it!

We are a people shaped by our religion. If we don't hang on
to our Law we'll just sink into the morass of pagan culture that
surrounds us. This Galilean undermines who we are, our
special calling. And what does he think he's doing sending out
his disciples like missionaries, and consorting with Gentiles,
like that Syro-Phoenician woman whose daughter he cured? I
suppose you'll be telling me that Isaiah approves of that too.

*You've read Isaiah, Nathaniel, you know what he says. God's
purpose is not just to restore the tribes of Jacob, to bring Israel back
to him, but to be a light to the nations, taking his salvation to earth's
farthest bounds.**

It's not surprising that that prophecy has been set aside. It
does not fit in with the Law, and would destroy our special
status. What would become of our festivals and seasons, like
Sabbath and Passover? They set us apart from the heathen. So
do the rules about what we eat and the way we prepare our
food – and, of course, the mark circumcised in our flesh.

I don't have to tell you this, Omri; you know we're not like
other nations. But Jesus ignores all these things that set us
apart. He transgresses all the rules: he says the Sabbath is
made for man and that he is Lord over the Sabbath; his
followers don't wash before meals, and now he says it doesn't
matter what you eat. How can he be sent by God if he breaks
the laws of God? Soon he'll be saying that circumcision is
nothing. And that will be the end of us!

*Has it never occurred to you, Nathaniel, that most Israelites – most
of this People set apart – can't keep all these rules? Not only are there
so many rules, but life would come to a standstill if we all followed
them all the time. Take the shepherds: there's no way a shepherd, out
in all weathers, can keep all the rules; but without shepherds there'd*

be no wool and you'd not have that fine robe you're wearing which is part of your identity as a Pharisee.

Can't you see? OK, the Law is about giving us a special identity. Yes, it's true that it sets us apart from other nations. God has sent us as a sign to the nations of the way he calls all people to live, not to isolate us from them. And the way the Law has been interpreted has placed a barrier not only between us and other nations, it has divided Israel itself. So many of our traditions keep us apart from one another. They entrench social division; they keep the privileged, privileged and the poor, poor. We're a long way from the united community of the Exodus. And we've made things worse with our oral tradition, piling up rules on top of the Law. We've created an instrument of division, not of unity.

I don't accept that for one minute. It's the failure of the people to live up to their calling that has entrenched division, not the Law. And, Omri, you're forgetting that we Pharisees have tried hard to soften the requirements of the Law so that the ordinary people can obey it. It's the Saduccees who are inflexible; Jesus should be attacking them, not us!

That may be true, but even our rules still bear hard on the mass of people. We're not really on the side of the ordinary people – we've never slackened the rules for table fellowship, have we? We're still an elite, and that's why Jesus attacks us.

What's wrong with elitism? Someone's got to uphold standards.

I'm all for standards, Nathaniel, but the question is: What are the right standards? What was it that Micah said? –

What shall I bring when I come before the LORD? Will the LORD be pleased with thousands of rams or ten thousand rivers of oil? The LORD has told you mortals what is good, and what is it that the LORD requires of you: only to act justly, to love loyalty, to walk humbly with your God.

[Micah 6.6–8]

We've lost sight of that, and we've equated our traditions with the Law itself. That's what makes Jesus so angry. I'm not surprised that he calls us hypocrites.

It's insufferable! He's no right...

I know it's hard to take – so direct and uncompromising – but we're not being true to the Lord if we reject what Jesus says with some knee-jerk reaction. Are we infallible? Are our standards necessarily the right ones? Is there nothing in what he says that we need to take to heart? After all, Israel doesn't have a good record when it comes to listening to the prophets. Maybe if we had we wouldn't be in this mess...

You and your prophets...

Nathaniel! You can't ignore the prophets. They recalled us to our true identity. Yes, we are a people set apart, but as a servant people, not as an exclusive people. All our traditions just keep us separate, not only from the nations, but also from one another. God – and Jesus – wants us to be true to our calling.

Look, Omri, this man is not a prophet; he's a carpenter. What do carpenters know about God or the Law? You're not telling me that God has chosen an untrained carpenter to teach us lessons, and from Nazareth, of all places! The Messiah is simply not coming from Nazareth – period! Nothing good ever came out of Nazareth!

Well, we had better leave it there. We're not going to agree. I know I'm in a minority; most Pharisees agree with you. What are you going to do about him?

It's not for me to decide, but he can't be allowed to go on like this. He has to be silenced!

16

THEY HAVE NOTHING TO EAT

Mark 6.30–56; 8.1–21

*Ignoring the opposition from the Pharisees, Jesus continued his work, teaching and healing. On two occasions, according to Mark, he fed large crowds of people. For those who were there, like **Levi**, the former tax-collector turned disciple,* it was unforgettable.*

WE were getting used to the crowds. Some of them followed Jesus for days at a time. They were hungry for his words, so much so that sometimes they forgot to eat! We'd come from Sidon into the territory of the Decapolis, Gentile lands on the opposite side of the lake, and found a remote place to rest. But, as usual, word soon spread that Jesus was there, and it wasn't long before a huge crowd gathered: about four thousand at a guess. Greeks, Jews, they all sought Jesus! They'd run out of food, but were loath to go away. Jesus felt for them, not wanting to send them away hungry. But how were we to feed them? As we said to him, 'How can anyone provide them with bread in this remote place?'

Now, this had happened before, over on the Jewish side of the lake, with another large crowd. On that occasion some of the people had a bit of food – five loaves and two fish. Jesus took it, blessed it, and gave it to us to distribute. Astonishingly, there was enough for everyone; no one went home hungry! So, the next time, when we found that a few of the Greeks did have a bit of food – seven loaves and a few small fish – I wondered if he would repeat the miracle. And he did. He took the bread and the fish, blessed it and gave it to us to distribute, and as before there was enough for everyone! There were even scraps left over – seven baskets full – a bit less than the twelve we'd collected on the other side. It was astonishing, but then we had come to expect astonishing things to happen when Jesus was around. We also expected him to ask us about – and he did!

As we rowed back across the lake, he warned us to be on our guard against the leaven of the Pharisees and the leaven of Herod. He often spoke in this way, and we hadn't a clue what he meant. All we could think about was that now we hadn't got enough bread to feed ourselves – we'd only got one loaf in the boat. Of course, we were hopelessly wide of the mark, and remained so even when he made us repeat the numbers: twelve baskets from the five thousand, and seven baskets from the four thousand. 'Do you still not understand?' he asked in exasperation. No one dared answer.

It was a repeat of what had happened after he'd fed the first crowd. He sent us off in the boats to Bethsaida while he dismissed the crowds. It seemed an odd thing to do – how was he going to get back? – but we did as he asked. The wind blew up, and it took all our effort to make any headway. We spent the night on the lake. And then the most extraordinary thing: we saw a ghost walking on the lake! We cried out in fear; the ghost answered: 'Take heart! It is I; do not be afraid.' It was Jesus. He got into the boat, the wind dropped, and we soon got to the shore. Nobody said anything; we didn't know what to make of it – not just walking on the lake, but also feeding five thousand people with just a few loaves and fishes. We didn't see these things as signs pointing to who he was.

It took a long time for the penny to drop. We should have guessed from the outset. When you look back on what he said and did, it was obvious what he was about, but we couldn't see it. Our upbringing had so formed our outlook that it provided a filter through which we saw the world and shaped our ideas of God, and of what it meant to be a Jew, that anything new was interpreted in accordance with accepted ideas.

The Pharisees – tradition is life for them – had the problem in spades! They challenged Jesus about how we ate with defiled hands – not doing the ritual cleansing before meals. You could see their total lack of comprehension when Jesus responded by accusing them of setting aside the commandments of God to maintain their traditions. He said the way they used corban nullified the fourth commandment: 'Honour your father and mother...' He was right, but that wasn't the way they looked at it. It was the same when they asked him for a sign from heaven: something that would put his authenticity and his authority beyond doubt. Well, if feeding five thousand people, just like the Israelites had been fed in the wilderness, wasn't a sign from heaven, I don't know what would be. But they just couldn't see it.

As I said, it took a long time for the penny to drop, for the filter to be taken away from our eyes. It was like the way he healed a blind man in two stages; our understanding came in stages too. Jesus had spoken about creating a new community; we thought he meant a reformed Israel – getting rid of corruption, reducing the power of the priests, giving us ordinary people a better life – but he wanted to take away the filter completely, and overcome all social and racial divisions. God's ideas, he said, were very different from those of the priests and the scribes. The prophets, like Micah, Isaiah, Jeremiah, and Ezekiel, saw things as God did, but the priests, the scribes and the Pharisees – and us – did not.

Jesus believed God wanted a single humanity brought together by their relationship to him, and not separated by social and racial divisions. Questions about who was acceptable to God and who was not were irrelevant; everyone was acceptable to God. Jesus showed this when he fed the Gentiles in the same way that he'd fed the Jews. Jesus was about reconciling Jew and Gentile: the priests and the others opposed integration on grounds of social and ritual purity. Herod and his group followed the same policy, but for different reasons; their ideas were about cultural superiority and collaboration with Rome. This was the leaven of the Pharisees and the leaven of Herod that Jesus referred to, and both would equally destroy the new community Jesus wanted to create.

I related to Jesus' vision; it touched me deeply. As a tax-collector I was an outsider, unacceptable to God, but with Jesus I knew that that wasn't true. I also know now that the conflict with the Pharisees was not just about their customs and traditions but went to the root of their whole understanding of God – and for whom he is God. As Jesus said, God makes the sun to shine on everyone. No-one, Jew or Gentile, is beyond his love.

17
WHAT DOES THE LORD REQUIRE?

Luke 14.7-24; 16.19-31; 19.11-27

Mark does not give as full account of Jesus' teaching as does Luke, and some of the parables recorded by Luke but omitted by Mark, e.g. the Lost Son and the Good Samaritan, feature in other episodes. In this episode we focus on some of the other Lukan parables that illustrate how Jesus' teaching challenged the people and rulers to look again at what God required.

Omri, *the sympathetic Pharisee in episode 15, sensing that events were approaching a climax, was among those who had gone to meet Jesus as he approached Jerusalem.*

MY conversation with Nathaniel had left me deeply disturbed. I suppose I ought not to have been surprised that people like him felt Jesus should be silenced, but his tone of voice was menacing; silencing someone like Jesus meant only one thing: death. The word had gone around that Jesus was on his way from Jericho to Jerusalem for Passover. It felt to me that things were moving to a climax – after all, he had said that it was unthinkable that a prophet should meet his death elsewhere than in Jerusalem. I wasn't one of his followers, but I respected him, and his teaching resonated with me. I wanted to be there.

I left the house early and made my way towards Bethphage. There was a place where people gathered, and sure enough, when I arrived there was already a small crowd waiting for Jesus. People recognised me as a Pharisee, and made way for me. It wasn't what I wanted. Jesus' words about the way we loved to be greeted in the street had found their mark with me, and although I had dressed as simply as I could, it was still clear who I was. But it enabled me to find a place to stand by a wall, and for that I was grateful. I introduced myself to the man next to me, rather to his surprise, I think. He had an interesting face; he said his name was Joel. It wasn't long before Jesus arrived with a group of followers. It was a convenient place to rest before entering Jerusalem, and seeing us gathered, he came over to speak to us.

Someone asked him if the Kingdom was about to dawn. In response he told a parable about a man of noble birth who went on a long journey to be appointed king, leaving his business affairs in the hands of his servants.* On his return he summoned them and asked what profit they had made. Two had done well and were rewarded; a third had not; he had simply kept safe the money he was given, and returned it as it was. The king was furious; he took the money and gave it to the one who had done the best. To the servants who protested that it was unfair, the king said, 'I tell you everyone who has will be given more; but whoever has nothing will forfeit even what he has.' And with that he mounted a donkey that had been brought for him, and began the descent to Jerusalem.

The crowd dispersed. Some followed Jesus, others returned to their business. I turned to say goodbye to Joel, but he wasn't ready to leave. He asked me what I made of the parable; he wasn't clear if Jesus thought the kingdom was about to dawn.

I remembered another occasion when Jesus was asked the same question: 'When the kingdom will come?' He replied, 'You cannot tell by observation when the kingdom of God comes. You cannot say, "Look, here it is," or "There it is." For the kingdom of God is among you.' [Luke 17.20–21]

'What did he mean by that?' Joel asked.

'Well,' I said, 'I think he meant that the kingdom of God isn't like an earthly kingdom – like under King David or the

Romans. It's not a state like the Zealots want to establish; it's more about the values you live by, the things that are in your heart.'

'I'll have to think about that,' Joel replied. 'It doesn't sound much like a kingdom to me!' Nor, I think, did it sound like a kingdom to most people, but since my argument with Nathaniel I'd thought a lot about what Jesus taught. He wasn't about overthrowing the priests and the scribes, or getting rid of the Romans; what he was about was inner transformation, a new spirit, that would transform the way we lived.

WE sat in silence, each with his own thoughts. Joel had been thinking along the same lines. 'So,' he said, 'if the kingdom is about the values we take to heart, then it's in our hearts that it must dawn. The kingdom is within us. So what about that parable he told. What was he saying about the kingdom? It sounded more like a time of reckoning with the king summoning his servants to give an account of what they had done while he was away.'

I wasn't sure how to reply. When Jesus spoke about a king or a Lord, he was speaking about God, and lots of his stories involved a reckoning. That was the climax of the story, and what stood out was the contrast in the way the king treated the bold and the cautious servants. Using what you were given in the service of the king was what Jesus commended; those who did not were not worthy of his trust, and forfeited even what they had. The values of the kingdom had to be put to use, not just admired and then ignored. I said something along these lines to Joel. He said it put him in mind of another parable that Jesus had told about a man who prepared a banquet and invited lots of people, but when the time came they all sent excuses. He was furious, and so, instead of his fine friends, he invited the poor, the crippled, the blind and the lame. 'I want my house full,' he said. 'I tell you, not one of those who were invited shall taste my banquet.'

'It's not quite the same,' Joel said, 'but it's another story about heaven, and it also has a reckoning. The guests did not value their invitations, so like the cautious servant, they forfeited their places. I guess they did not have the right values in their hearts.'

Joel had to go, and he left me with my thoughts as I made my way home.

I too, had heard that parable about the great banquet. Like the one we'd heard today, I'd felt it more personally; it was directed at us Pharisees, and at the scribes and the lawyers. We were the ones too preoccupied with keeping the rules, maintaining our tradition, that we'd lost sight of the goal. It was the poor people, like Joel, who were closer to God in their hearts than we were. I agreed with Jesus that the kingdom was among us already, latent in the values of the Law, in the words of the prophets, but we were too concerned to maintain our tradition than to take the risks necessary really to bring it to birth. The more I thought about it, the more it seemed to me that the parable of the servants was an indictment of our lack of courage. That third servant was a picture of us pious Jews who seek security in the a meticulous observance of the law, tithing mint and cummin to win merit in the sight of God. We take pride in the way we kept ourselves apart, but it has made our religion barren. We were doing nothing to increase God's capital, just hoarding it; not only were the ordinary people not benefitting, we were deriving no benefit ourselves.

As I sat and reflected, I found myself thinking about another parable that Jesus told, about a rich man who ignored the poor man at his gate. At the time I was so angered by it that I'd put it out of my mind, but now it came back to me. They both died; the rich man went to hell, and Lazarus, the poor man, to heaven. I could hear the rich man crying out to Abraham to send Lazarus to assuage his torment. Abraham's reply was chilling: 'There is a great gulf fixed between us; no one can cross it from our side to reach you, and none may pass from your side to us.' And when he asks that his brothers be warned of their fate if they did not mend their ways, Abraham says, 'They have Moses and the prophets; let them listen to them. And if they don't listen to them, then they will pay no heed even if someone were to visit them from the dead.'

Jesus was unsettling me. Was all that I held dear – tradition, status, learning – just so much garbage,* leading me down the wrong path? 'They have Moses and the prophets…' Jesus placed himself in the line of the prophets. The words of Micah that I'd learned from my father came back to me:

> The Lord has told you what is good, and what is it that the
> Lord requires of you: only to act justly, to love loyalty, to
> walk humbly with your God.   [Micah 6.8]

Jesus was putting flesh on those words. I was troubled in my spirit: which side of the gulf was I on?

IV
Journey to Jerusalem

They drew near to Jericho. *Mark 10.46*

18
WHO DO YOU SAY THAT I AM?

Mark 8.27-9.8

After the feeding of the four thousand, Jesus and the disciples set out for the villages of Caesarea Philippi in the far north of Israel. It was the beginning of a long journey that would bring them to Jerusalem in time for the Passover festival. For a time Jesus avoided the crowds, concentrating on preparing the disciples for what was to come. At the end of the first week Jesus was transfigured. It was a week of testing encounters, as **Peter** recalls.*

SOMETHING had happened. As we set out for Caesarea Philippi there was a different mood in the group. We were still smarting from Jesus' exasperation at our lack of understanding, but it was deeper than that: a shadow seemed to have fallen across our path. When Jesus first called us we had been full of joy and optimism; but the path he'd led us on wasn't what we'd been expecting. The gratitude of the crowds was wonderful but it was becoming clear that that was not the reality we had to deal with; what we had to deal with was the attitude of the authorities, and gratitude was the last thing on their minds.

We seemed to move continually between light and darkness. There were the crowds whose lives were lit up by Jesus, and there were the authorities whose intentions were black. There was the blinding light of clarity on the mountain, and there was our total failure to see clearly as we walked on the road. One of the worst of these moments for me was when we were on the way to Caesarea Philippi. Jesus asked us who the people said he was, and then more pointedly he asked, 'And you, who do you say that I am?' My answer was instant: 'You are the Messiah.' But it rapidly became clear that our ideas about the Messiah were very different.

I knew that Jesus was not the Messiah of general expectation, a saviour who would restore the political fortunes of Israel, but I hadn't thought much beyond this, and when he said that he would endure great suffering and be rejected, I seized hold of him and said, 'No, this can't happen to you!' I'll never forget his rebuke (although it wasn't just for me: he looked round and included all of us): 'Out of my sight, Satan! You think as men think, not as God thinks.' Later we realised that Jesus saw himself as the Servant of Isaiah's prophecy whose task was to bring Israel back to the LORD *[Isaiah 42.1–4]*. We thought of the Messiah as a conqueror; Jesus thought of him as a servant.

His biting rebuke was the first thing which made me realise that something had happened that week. The second was his renewed call to follow him. 'Whoever wants to be a follower of mine,' he said, 'must renounce self; he must take up his cross and follow me.'

This chilled us to the bone. We all knew what he meant, who would have to take up their cross. It wasn't a figure of speech about bearing insults or undeserved burdens, it was literal: it meant crucifixion. Those who demanded freedom from oppression, even if they did so in the name of God, could expect to be made a public example and die on a cross. This was how the Romans punished political dissidents and trouble-makers, anyone who had to be suppressed so that law and order could be preserved. The guerrilla fighters who fought an insurgent campaign against the Romans were all crucified.

At first we were stupefied. We couldn't really believe that Jesus was calling us to crucifixion. The thought of excruciating pain and total humiliation consumed me. But if you followed the logic of his words and deeds – that his way was superior to the Jewish Law and traditions – it became obvious that he and his followers were regarded as dissidents, and were at risk of being punished as such. Through him, Jesus said, God was engaged in a spiritual battle, not merely at the personal level, but against the spirit of the age. The difference between him and the guerrillas was that he did not seek political power for himself; evil would be overcome not by violence but by sacrifice. As he said, 'Whoever wants to save his life will lose it, but whoever loses his life for my sake and for the gospel's will save it.' This hardly made things easier!

Darkness seemed to envelope us. Jesus chose this moment to take James and John and me apart. He led us up a mountain. At the top we had the most astonishing vision: we saw him transfigured and talking to Moses and Elijah, and we heard a voice that said, 'This is my beloved Son; listen to him.' It was overwhelming; we were terrified. I blurted out some nonsense about making shelters for the three of them, but I spoke as a fool. The three of us talked about it afterwards: What had we seen? We didn't really know, but it seemed that we were being told that Jesus was indeed the Messiah; his words were true and they were life; and his way was the way of God.

Something had happened that week. There was the bitter misunderstanding, but then a second call to follow him, and a second voice from heaven telling us to listen to him. We had moved into the dark.

19
I HAVE FAITH!

Mark 9.9-32 + 7.31-37

On their way down the mountain, Jesus told Peter, James and John not to speak of what they had witnessed until he had risen from the dead. Mark says they 'seized upon those words, and discussed among themselves what this "rising from the dead" could mean.'*

During their absence, some people had brought an epileptic boy to be healed. The disciples had tried, but failed. By the time Jesus and the others had returned, a large crowd had gathered, including some scribes who were arguing with the disciples. Jesus restored the boy to wholeness, driving out the demon. When asked by the disciples why they had not been able to do so, he replied, 'This kind cannot be driven out except by prayer.'

After the resurrection, when Peter, James and John had shared their experience of the Transfiguration with the others, **Thomas** *talked about the meaning of the two episodes with Johanan,* one of the followers of Jesus, as he relates:*

WE had all wondered what had happened on the mountain, that day when we'd tried to cure the boy with the dumb spirit, but all the three of them would say was, 'We can't speak about it now; we'll tell you later.' Although something momentous had clearly happened, their lips were sealed, and we forgot about it. And then, after Jesus was raised, they did tell us. I found myself alone with Johanan. Like me, he wanted to probe the meaning of all that we had seen and heard, and we naturally sought each other's company. I said to him, 'Do you remember how we seized upon the words, "risen from the dead". And how we kept on asking ourselves what Jesus was talking about?'

Johanan agreed. Rising from the dead made no more sense to us than Jesus' conviction that his destiny was to suffer. After the cure of the epileptic boy he took us on a secret journey through Galilee to teach us about it. 'The Son of Man is now to be handed over into the power of men,' he said, 'and they will kill him; and three days after being killed, he will rise again.' But we didn't understand; it simply didn't tie in with our understanding of the Messiah. As I said to Johanan, we had got it wrong so many times that we were afraid to ask him anything for fear of looking foolish.

'It was like that on the mountain,' he replied. 'They didn't understand why Jesus forbade them to tell the rest of us what they had experienced; but they kept quiet. I can see now, that in order to be able to speak about it they needed to understand its meaning. It wasn't difficult to guess that "rising from the dead" had something to do with Jesus' prediction of his death and the coming of the Messiah. And then, later, talking to Peter and James, I recalled something that scribe Ehud had said. He dismissed the idea that Jesus could be the Messiah because Elijah had not come first. 'Did you ask him about that?' I said.

'Yes, we did,' said James, hesitantly.

'And what did he reply?'

'He said, "Elijah will come first to set everything right. However, I tell you Elijah has already come, and they have done to him what they wanted, as the scriptures say of him."'

That was just so typical of Jesus. Sometimes we got a straight reply, but often we were left with an elliptical saying that left us to work things out for ourselves.

Johanan continued: 'Why on earth, Thomas, didn't we grasp that he was talking about his cousin John who baptised him at the Jordan? You know, it's only now, talking to you, that I've put the two events together! As we weren't there at the time, it wasn't part of our experience, so I hadn't thought about it. But there was a voice from heaven on that occasion too.'

'Yes, so I believe: "You are my beloved Son; in you I take delight". Was that what the three of them heard on the mountain?'

'Almost the same: "This is my beloved Son; listen to him." I see it now, Thomas. It's all of a piece! The One in whom God delights is the One who speaks his words. By raising him from the dead God made it clear that his words were God's own words, that Jesus is the true and living way.' *[John 14.6]*

'That's a good phrase!' I exclaimed. Johanan was good with words, and had good insights. But what I really wanted to talk about was the vision, so I asked him how he understood the meaning of Jesus being transfigured, and Moses and Elijah appearing with him.

'Yes, I've thought about that. I think it's all about light. Like David said in the psalms, God is enfolded in a robe of light:

> Lord my God, you are very great,
> clothed in majesty and splendour,
> and enfolded in a robe of light.   *[Psalm 104.1b–2a]*

'That's how they saw Jesus: enfolded in a robe of light. It was a vision of him as he truly is: the Son of Man is the Son of God, the Messiah. Elijah was there as the forerunner, and Moses was there because Jesus fulfilled God's promise, given through Moses, to raise up another prophet who will lead his people to freedom. But more than that, Thomas, more than that. He gives us more than Moses: the law was given through Moses, but grace and truth have come through Jesus.' *[John 1.17]*

Again, Johanan, though not an eye-witness, had seen things clearly. But light was beginning to dawn for me, too: if he referred to his rising from the dead, he must have known what was going to happen. He had tried to tell us – the vision of light was a confirmation of all that he said – but he knew we wouldn't really understand until he had been raised, and the light had dawned.

OUR conversation moved on to what happened when we joined the others. It was always the way: when Jesus wasn't there, something went wrong! People knew that Jesus was around, and, as always, they brought the sick for healing. By now they also knew who we were, and stories had been going around of the cures we had been able to perform in Jesus' name when he had sent us out to the villages. On this occasion, as Jesus wasn't present, they asked us to help. A man had brought his son. He was possessed by a spirit that made him dumb and threw him into convulsions. It was pretty frightening; he looked quite lifeless. We tried to cast out the spirit, but failed. The scribes took the opportunity to denounce us, repeating their jibe that Jesus cast out spirits by Beelzebub. We refuted this vehemently, and it all became very heated!

Fortunately, at this moment, Jesus returned. The effect he had on the crowd was extraordinary. They were overcome with awe and ran to him, in marked contrast to their attitude to the scribes. People avoided them because they treated them with disdain. As Jesus approached, the evil spirit threw the boy on to the ground. It was as though it recognised Jesus and his authority over evil. The boy rolled around, foaming at the mouth.

The boy's father explained that he had the condition from birth, and pleaded with Jesus for help. 'If it is possible for you,' he said, 'take pity on us and help us.' His cry was heart-rending.

'If it is possible!' said Jesus. 'Everything is possible to one who has faith.'

I'll never forget the father's reply: 'I have faith; help me where faith falls short.' Jesus cast out the spirit. It didn't go quietly. It threw the boy into repeated convulsions, and left him looking like a corpse. Many thought he was dead, but Jesus took him by the hand and raised him to his feet. His father, weak with relief and overwhelmed with gratitude, led him away.

'I remember that father,' said Johanan. 'Few people pleaded with Jesus as he did, straight from the heart. And his words were like an arrow to my heart: "I have faith; help me where faith falls short." "Me too!" I said to myself.'

'We all felt the same,' I said. 'We believed, but our faith also fell short. That must have had something to do with why we couldn't cast out the demon.'

Johanan agreed: 'I think it had everything to do with it. Do you remember; we asked Jesus about it? He said, "This kind cannot be driven out, except by prayer."'

'Another of his unexplained sayings!' I interjected.

'Exactly! I've thought about it, on and off, ever since. It seems to me, Thomas, that the authority Jesus had over deep-seated evil came from his own deep relationship with God, and that came from the depth of his prayer – all those times when he spent long hours in prayer. Because of that, he was able to access the same power from God that raised him from the dead. Maybe, that's why Peter and the others had to wait before they could share the experience of his transfiguration. It only made sense when we had seen him raised. Only then could we grasp – not just with our minds, but with the whole of our being – that the power that raised him was the same power by which he healed and which gave him his authority. He was the resurrection and the life.' *[John 11.25]*

IT WASN'T just about light, about seeing clearly; it was also about really hearing his words and taking them to heart -- and having the courage to speak. Jesus had made this clear when he healed a man who was deaf and had an impediment in his speech, but we hadn't seen beyond the healing to the truth to which it pointed. Time and again he said, 'If you have ears to hear, then hear.' But our ears were muffled, our sight was dull, and our tongues were tied. On the mountain the vision and the voice came from the cloud, but at the time the three of them were simply awestruck, cowering under the clouds that over-shadowed them. Jesus' transfiguration was a shaft of light in a scene of increasing darkness. The clarity it offered lay in the future, after he was raised; then we were in the dark, our minds shrouded by the limits of our experience. All we knew was that around Jesus the shadows were deepening.

20
ONE THING YOU LACK

Mark 10.13-31

As the journey continued towards Jerusalem, Jesus' teaching about discipleship became more challenging. As we have seen, his ideas about God, family, the Law and social relationships stood accepted ideas on their heads. The new community that Jesus came to create was (and is) so different from accepted attitudes and values that the disciples failed completely to connect with what he said. In the encounter with the rich stranger who ran up and asked what he had to do to gain eternal life, Jesus once again rejected accepted ideas, as **Levi** explains.*

WE twelve were a very diverse group, very different characters and backgrounds, but we were united in one thing: life had not been easy for us. None of us was well-off; socially we were on the lowly side, just ordinary folk. People in Jerusalem looked down on us Galileans, but that didn't matter at all to Jesus. Thinking about it afterwards, it seemed to me that choosing us was quite deliberate; he wanted to show that the accepted marks of status – family, money, land, power, prestige – were of no account to God. As it says in the scriptures, God's special concern was for the poor: widows and orphans and strangers, those without resources or status. Jesus was clear that this special concern meant more than extending charity to them; it meant building a new community in which their needs would be met and their lack of status taken away. The way he had accepted me, a social outcast – one of the lost sheep – and treated me as the equal of the others was a sign of what this new community would be like. I think we all felt the same in our different ways, but even so, we struggled to understand quite what this new community amounted to.

There was that day when, just as we were setting out on a journey, one of the local landowners ran up to Jesus, knelt before him and asked what he must do to gain eternal life. Now this man was top of the tree. Landowners were the most powerful social class, they didn't kneel for anyone! And he was pious: he said he'd kept all the commandments since he was a boy – I don't think any of us could have claimed that! He must have been carrying a real burden to seek help in that way. You could tell that Jesus' heart went out to him, but he told him plainly he had to sell everything and give the money to the poor, and then become one of Jesus' followers. You could feel his heart sink; this was not what he was expecting to hear. His face fell, he turned, and went away.

Our faces fell too. Jesus noticed this immediately; he turned to us and said, 'How hard it will be for the wealthy to enter the kingdom of God!' He said it as though it was obvious; but it wasn't at all obvious to us. We believed, like everyone else, that wealth was synonymous with blessing from God, and here was Jesus saying precisely the opposite! It would be easier, he said, for a camel to pass through the eye of needle than for the rich to enter the kingdom. We were astonished. If the rich couldn't make it to heaven, then who could be saved?

At the time the implication was lost on us, but Jesus was clearly saying, as he had made plain to the landowner, that personal piety alone was not going to get anyone to heaven, only concrete acts of justice. So, for the rich to be saved they must redistribute their wealth and stop oppressing the poor. Well, that wasn't going to happen any time soon! Would it ever happen? I think many of us were beginning to wonder if Jesus had got things right. He accepted none of the ideas that were commonly believed. How on earth could his ideas become reality? His answer was that salvation was the gift of God: 'For men it is impossible, but not for God; everything is possible for God.'

Peter, as ever, spoke the thoughts of us all: 'What about us, he asked, 'we have left everything to follow you.' And we had. Asking a fisherman to leave his nets, or me to stop collecting taxes, is the same as asking that landowner to give away all that he has. Well, we'd done it! We'd left our homes, family, land – all the things that are counted by us Jews as almost more important than life itself – we'd left everything to follow him; so, where did that leave us? Were we assured of a place in the kingdom? Yes, said Jesus, our sacrifice would be rewarded a hundredfold, *in this life*, but we would know persecutions too; and in the age to come our place in the kingdom was assured.

I'm not sure what we made of this. We had no choice, we'd burned our boats and there was no turning back, but the road ahead was much harder than any of us had anticipated when we first responded to the call. Jesus was a long way from the Messiah of popular expectation. The Messiah was expected to save Israel as it was, not to turn its ways and ideas upside down. I hadn't really thought through the implications of the way Jesus reached out to people like me. He was identifying himself with the poor and rejected; this was what he meant when he said he had been sent to the lost sheep of the house of Israel *[Matthew 15.24]*. That sounded fine. Those of us who felt oppressed wanted to feel included. We dreamed often of radical social change, but finding ourselves expected to be the agents of that change was quite another matter. I didn't think I'd signed up for that!

21

I CAME TO SERVE

Mark 9.33-10.16; 10.32-45

*The journey to Jerusalem sets the scene for what will happen there,
and as they travelled, Jesus tried for the last time to get the disciples
to understand his vision of the Messiah. But accepted ideas were just
too engrained; his teaching was heard by uncomprehending minds.
Although **James** was one of the inner three, he understood no better
than the rest, as he explains:*

AS WE made our way to Jerusalem there was a charged
atmosphere in the group. You could feel that things were
coming to a climax; some of us were awestruck, others afraid.
The prospect of an ending took me back to the beginning,
when John and I had been called at the lakeside. Being with
Jesus was an incredible experience. We'd seen wonders that,
had we not seen them with our own eyes, we would have said
were impossible, most amazingly restoring the dead to life!
And we'd heard teaching that surpassed in its authority
anything that we'd heard before, from the scribes or from
anyone. And the crowds – it seemed, then, that the whole
people were with us. This man must be the Messiah; surely we
were on the threshold of the Age of Liberation of which we'd
dreamed! If the new age was to dawn there would be conflict,
and we were prepared for that.

What we weren't prepared for was Jesus' vision of the
Messiah. As we approached Jerusalem I wondered what Jesus
made of the twelve he had chosen. He'd been so exasperated
with us since we left Galilee, he must have asked himself if

he'd chosen the right people. Our problem was that we'd been formed by centuries of tradition. Our ideas, our hopes and dreams had been shaped by a culture of separateness. We weren't like other nations, and we bitterly resented their domination of us. God for us was a warrior; we'd been brought up on stories of him defeating our enemies, and that's what we were expecting of Jesus. Of course, this would mean overcoming our leaders, who saw co-operation with the Romans as the best option. It wasn't clear how this was to be achieved, but so far Jesus had shown himself more than a match for them. What we hadn't grasped, and this was especially true of John and me, was that Jesus didn't see it like this at all.

There had been signs, but we hadn't really seen them. He'd said many things trying to make his message plain: we had to be like children if we wanted to enter the kingdom of heaven; those who were first would be last and the last first; don't even think about who is the greatest, greatness is about service, not status; men and women are equal partners in marriage; cut off your hand or your foot if it leads you astray; tear out your eye if your eye causes your downfall; it is better to enter into life maimed than to be led astray. Like all of us, he exaggerated to make his point, but even so, we hadn't got the point.

We tried hard to get on to Jesus' wavelength, but we still got it very wrong. On one occasion John said to him that that they had seen a man driving out demons in his name and they had tried to stop him, because 'he was not one of us.' Jesus wasn't concerned with that sort of clan mentality. Anyone who believed in him – who was not against him – he accepted as being on his side. He corrected John: 'Do not stop him, for no one who performs a miracle in my name will be able the next moment to speak evil of me.' He said we must have salt within ourselves and be at peace with one another. And all the time he was telling us that in Jerusalem he would meet his death.

We simply hadn't understood. All this talk of suffering and being put to death made no sense to us; it seemed incredible that Jesus with his miraculous powers would not overcome those who opposed him. The accepted belief about the Messiah governed our minds, and we were still expecting a Messianic coup. Our thoughts turned naturally to the new regime. John and I were strong characters; Jesus had called us *Boanerges,* 'Sons of Thunder'. We were natural leaders and we had been chosen with Peter to be Jesus' closest companions. The kingdom would need us, so we asked if the positions of honour could be ours when Jesus sat in glory.

I cringe when I think of it now; it was an appalling thing to ask, and showed just how little we'd grasped of his teaching. We were willing to suffer with him – God knows that we were – but that was not enough; we had no idea what we were asking.

The others were indignant; not that they understood any better. They were just furious that we were trying to place ourselves above them. Jesus tried again to teach us about leadership, and again he stood accepted ideas on their heads: it wasn't about lording it over others and making your authority felt; it was about humbling yourself. The true leader was the servant of those whom he led, willing to suffer for them.

We would have understood better if we had taken the words of Isaiah to heart. He spoke of the servant of the Lord who was despised and shunned, pain-wracked and afflicted with suffering, but who in truth was bearing our afflictions, and by whose wounds we are healed. 'We had all strayed like sheep,' he said, 'each of us going his own way, but the Lord laid on him the guilt of us all.' *[Isaiah 53.6]*

And this was how it would end, as Jesus said to us as we walked with him: 'The Son of Man did not come to be served but to serve, and to give his life as a ransom for many.'

22
WHAT DO YOU WANT?

Mark 10.46–52

There are two routes from Galilee to Jerusalem: the shorter one across Samaria, or the longer one via the Jordan valley. Jesus and the disciples took the longer route, walking along the valley to Jericho, about fifteen miles east of Jerusalem. As they approached the town a blind beggar called out to him. **Andrew** recalls the encounter:*

'WHAT do you want me to do for you?' That's what Jesus asked him. I thought what he wanted was clear enough, but sometimes Jesus asked these questions – I think he was making a point. The man was a beggar, and blind too; we found out later that his name was Bartimaeus. He was sitting by the roadside with his cloak spread out, as beggars do, to collect the coins thrown to him. He might have been blind, but there was no trouble with his voice; when he called out you could have heard him streets away. They tried to shut him up, but he shouted even louder, 'Son of David, have pity on me!'

'Son of David,' no one else on our journeys had called Jesus that. 'Son of David,' it hung in the air. What had this blind beggar sensed about Jesus? Had he seen something that the sighted had missed? Maybe that's why Jesus stopped and called him. The response was extraordinary; he threw off his cloak – more of a rag than a garment – jumped up, and came to Jesus. In answer to Jesus' question, he said, 'I want my sight back.' And Jesus said quite simply, 'Your faith has healed you.'

Instantly his sight returned and, stepping into the road, he followed us.

I don't know what became of Bartimaeus; I think he followed us all the way to Jerusalem; after that he was lost in the crowd. But the question Jesus asked him has stayed with me: 'What is it that you want me to do for you? What was it that I wanted him to do for me? Back at the beginning, in Galilee, when Jesus first called us, all I knew was that I wanted a new beginning: getting rid of the Romans and the corruption among our leaders. Back then, where we were headed seemed pretty clear. But the longer we spent with Jesus the more it became apparent that we weren't very good at seeing clearly – at least, not at seeing things as Jesus saw them. It became painfully clear at Caesarea Philippi when Jesus rounded on my brother Peter, saying he had completely missed the point about the Messiah. The rest of us had kept quiet; we'd all been thinking the same as Peter! Jesus was near exasperation when he heard that we'd been arguing about who was the greatest, and again when James and John had asked for the chief seats when Jesus came into his glory. When they approached him, he'd asked them the same question: 'What do you want me to do for you?' They'd asked for power and position; Bartimaeus had asked only to see clearly.

By the time we got to Jericho we no longer had a clear idea of who Jesus was and what he was about. It seems to me that Jesus' question was directed as much to us as to Bartimaeus: 'What do you want me to do for you?' Now, my answer would be the same as his: 'I want my sight back. I want to see clearly; I want to see things as you see them.'

I know now that this means a big change of outlook, a change of spirit, just as Jesus had told the rich young man to sell all that he had and give to the poor. It wasn't so much the young man's wealth that was wrong, but his spirit. It was his way of looking at life, his status and social attitudes, and that strange, confident piety that wealth engenders, that prevented him from seeing clearly. He needed a new spirit. He couldn't follow Jesus, but Bartimaeus could; he left his cloak, his only possession, and the money in it, behind, and followed in the way. It's the blind beggars who know their need of God; they're the ones who see clearly!

V

Passover & Passion

'Father, take this cup from me...' Mark 14.36

23
BETHANY

Luke 19.1-10, 28-48; Mark 11.1-11

*The Passover is the most important festival in the Jewish calendar. It celebrates the Exodus, the deliverance of the Israelites from slavery in Egypt to freedom in the Promised Land, as we saw in episode 2. Every year thousands of Jews came from all over Israel to Jerusalem for the festival. As Jesus and his disciples made their way there, they would have been part of this large pilgrimage. Among those who also made the journey were Amos and Sarah, the couple who went to the Jordan and were baptised by John (episode 5). They lodged with Amos' cousin Nabal, who lived at Bethany, not far from the city. **Amos** takes up the story.*

WE don't go to Jerusalem for Passover every year, but when we heard that the prophet Jesus would be there, we decided that this year we had go. We're lucky, we can stay with my cousin Nabal. It saves us the expense of taking lodgings, but we give him a bit to help out. It's about three years since we went to the Jordan that day when Jesus was baptized, and the memory of it is still vivid. We've heard a lot about him since then, but it's hard to be sure of what you hear – stories get embroidered in the telling – but if half of what we have heard is true, then he has done some truly wonderful things.

But he's also become the focus of controversy. People are divided, for and against him. It's sad, but anyone who challenges the powers in the land is bound to be attacked by them. Some people want him dead. 'The only good prophet is a dead prophet,' I heard someone say. But others believe he is the Messiah. I remember our friend Rachel asking me after our baptism if I thought he was the Messiah. I wasn't sure then; I'm still not sure; though, as I say, if half the things he's done are true... well, it makes you think. Perhaps he is... but then again, he's not the kind of Messiah we are expecting.

Passover is an important time for us, the sort of moment God would choose to reveal the Messiah. Maybe we'll know for sure by the end of the festival.

WE arrived at Nabal's house a few days before Passover began. He makes olive oil, and had just returned from Jericho where he'd been to the market. He had an extraordinary story to tell. While he was there, word went round that Jesus was coming, and a large crowd gathered in the market place. The authorities may not like him, but he's popular with the people; crowds flock to see him and hang on his words. I've never seen anyone with a bigger following. Nabal said those at the back stood on the stalls to get a better view, and someone even climbed into a tree.

It wasn't long before Jesus arrived with a large group following him. He paused, looking for a good place to stand, when he caught sight of the man in the tree. 'Who's that?' he asked. Someone hissed, 'Zacchaeus, the tax collector,' and spat on the ground. Nabal said he was a superintendent of taxes, and very rich. (Tax officials make a percentage on all they collect. They are hated!) To everyone's astonishment Jesus walked towards the tree and called out: 'Zacchaeus, be quick, and come down; I must come and stay with you today.' The crowd were aghast. There was a lot of murmuring; Jesus was going to be the guest of a sinner!

Well, Nabal said, Zacchaeus practically fell out of the tree, and, to general astonishment, said to Jesus, 'Here and now, sir, I give half my possessions to charity; and if I have defrauded anyone, I will repay him four times over.' That silenced the crowd. No one had ever heard a tax collector admit to cheating, nor offering to repay them fourfold – nor calling someone 'sir'. No wonder Jesus replied, 'Today salvation has come to this house.' And then, more pointedly – looking his critics in the face – he added: 'For this man too is a son of Abraham. The Son of Man came to seek and to save what is lost.' I don't imagine that was enough to end the murmuring; people don't like being put right. You can see why Jesus attracts controversy!

But Zacchaeus was not all that Jesus had noticed. He'd also seen Nabal with his donkey, and when he found out he lived at Bethany, asked if he could use it the next day when he was going to ride into Jerusalem. He said he'd send a couple of his disciples to collect it, and they agreed a password: 'Our Master needs it and will send it back here without delay.'

Jesus did stay with Zacchaeus that night, and the next day he set out for Jerusalem. By the time he reached Bethphage and Bethany it was well on into the afternoon, and he rested while his disciples collected Nabal's donkey. Some of the people with him had walked all the way from Jericho; others had joined him along the route, so there was a large crowd with him, and an atmosphere of great excitement. You could feel it rolling along the road as they approached. No one in living memory had ever seen a great prophet enter the city, and they wanted to be part of it. Sarah and I, Nabal and his wife and family – we all wanted to be part of it. It felt as though all Bethany and Bethphage were there!

Standing, waiting for Jesus to arrive, I listened to the talk, and it made me wonder: How committed was his support? Some, clearly, didn't know who he was, they just happened to be around. Others were critical: How could he be the Messiah without an army? Some were real disciples – I recognised a few faces from two years ago – but most of us were there out of curiosity, or drawn by the sense of occasion. If something happened, we wanted to be able to say, 'I was there!' I've seen other popular leaders, and the way they attracted the crowds, and how everyone deserted them when things got tough. Jesus stood head and shoulders above them, and the crowds were much bigger, but would he fare any better? And what was his objective? By choosing to ride a donkey instead of a horse, Jesus was showing clearly that he came in peace,* but confrontation with the authorities seemed inevitable; would all these people be there when he needed them? Would I be there...?

At that moment the disciples came with the donkey, and the crowd parted to let Jesus through. There was a great shout of joy! Those nearest spread their cloaks on the donkey, and Jesus mounted. As he rode down the Mount of Olives into the city, he carried with him our hopes for peace. I've never been in such a joyful crowd. The road was carpeted with cloaks and brushwood from the fields; some waved palms, and shouted with joy: 'Hosanna! Blessings on him who comes in the name of the Lord! Blessings on the kingdom of our father David which is coming! Hosanna in the heavens.'

THIS was the prelude to a Passover like no other I had experienced. As I said to Sarah and Nabal when the day was over, what Jesus was saying through the way he entered the city seemed clear enough: he came as the Messiah, and he came in peace. But our mood deepened as we wondered what the chief priests and the scribes would make of it.

24
COURT OF THE GENTILES

Mark 11.12-25

By the time Jesus reached the Temple in Jerusalem it was late in the day, and he returned to Bethany with his disciples. The next morning, he returned to Jerusalem. St Mark sets the scene with the story of the fig tree. Feeling hungry, Jesus saw a fig tree in leaf and went up to it hoping to find some figs. There were none, which was not surprising as it was not the season for figs. Even so, Jesus said to the tree: 'May no one ever again eat fruit from you!' Mark adds, 'And his disciples were listening,' indicating clearly this was a significant saying. What the disciples made of it is not recorded, but it presaged what was about to happen in Jerusalem. Jesus' point was there is no season for responding to God; there is no one time of year to bring forth the fruits of the Spirit; every day we must be open to God and bring forth good fruit. But were Israel and her leaders ready to respond to God on this day, when he came to his Temple? Alas, they were not.*

Jesus went straight to the Court of the Gentiles, where people could change money into the special Temple currency used for offerings and to buy animals and birds for sacrifice. He drove out all the dealers, overturning their tables, and then, turning to the people, he said to them: 'Does not scripture say, "My house shall be called a house of prayer for all nations"? But you have made it a robbers' cave.' **Isaac**, *one of the pigeon traders, was furious.*

I'D never seen anything like it! I mean, this was the Temple of Jerusalem, not some small-town synagogue beyond the Styx, and there was this man – Jesus of Nazareth they called him – going berserk: shouting, throwing over tables and chairs, driving all the traders out of the courtyard. There was money all over the pavement, broken cages and pigeons flying free, people running away scared. There was so much noise and chaos it was hard to believe that it was all caused by just one man.

The LORD knows I was angry! I had no income for many days afterwards, not to mention loosing all my pigeons, and there was no compensation! But in the end it didn't make much difference. We cleared the place up, sorted ourselves out, and soon it was business as usual. I was pleased when they got rid of him. Nothing but a trouble-maker!

I COULDN'T understand it, but not everyone felt the same. My friend Joel was more on Jesus' side. He'd been talking to his friend Omri, one of the Pharisees, who felt the same. Well, Joel and me were talking about it some time afterwards. I hadn't quite heard what Jesus was shouting, but Joel had: something about us making the Temple a robbers' cave when it was meant to be a house of prayer for all nations. Apparently it was a quote from the prophet Jeremiah – not that that made any difference. 'House of prayer for all nations...' I'd never thought about it like that. To me, the 'Court of the Gentiles', where we traders were, was just a name; the Temple was really for the Jews.

But Joel's words stayed with me. Was what we were doing wrong?

I got our rabbi to show me the scroll of Jeremiah. Sure enough, there were the words Jesus had used. Jeremiah had condemned those who said one thing and did another: living immoral lives in the week and coming to the Temple on the sabbath as though they'd done nothing wrong. He said they were no better than robbers: 'Do you regard this house that bears my name as a bandits' cave?' What God wanted, he said, was a change of heart: fair dealing, care of the poor and the stranger, and moral lives, not outward show with no inner conviction *[Jeremiah 7.1-11]*. Joel said that's exactly what he'd heard Jesus say on many occasions.

AT the time I thought the priests had got rid of him because he was a trouble-maker, but now I'm not so sure. He didn't actually cause trouble; the threat he represented was more potential than actual. It was implicit in the way he set himself up as a rival source of authority saying people did not have to obey the food laws, or the sabbath laws. 'The sabbath was made for man', he said, 'not man for the sabbath.' And he behaved as though he had a direct line to God. He called himself the 'Son of Man', as though somehow he embodied the whole human race. Some even said he was the Messiah.

Well, I see it more clearly now. He was too much for the establishment; too big a challenge to their power, that's why they got rid of him. If he'd had his way there would have been no place for the priests and the scribes, nor indeed for us traders. Joel said Jesus taught that everyone was acceptable to God without sacrifice or offering. God's Spirit was within us, and we could work out what was right and wrong for ourselves. The Law that was so important to the scribes and the Pharisees, made God into a hard judge, but actually, according to Jesus God was a loving father, quick to forgive and slow to condemn. They didn't want to hear that!

Looking back on it, that morning in the Temple was the beginning of the end for Jesus. Ever since he came on the scene they'd been out to get him, and by the end of the week he was dead. But there was something about Jesus that I can't get out of my mind and which doesn't let me rest easy. I became a Temple trader because our father had been one. As the eldest son I followed in his steps without thinking about the rights and wrongs of it. The priests seemed happy enough – actually they'd set up the whole system, and it depended on us traders. We sold the pigeons and the animals for sacrifice, and changed people's money into the special Temple currency so they could make their offerings. Like most people, I just accepted it: that was how things were. We just wanted a quiet life. Ethics and theology are for those who have got time for them.

Well, I see things a bit differently now. We can't ignore these deep questions; if we do, we end up on the wrong track. I think that's what Jesus was really saying: we were on the wrong track. God is not just God of the Jews, but of all peoples. And Jeremiah was right: God is more concerned about justice and morality than our religious ritual. Many were up to far worse than us pigeon traders, and for those who paraded their piety religion seemed to be a matter of outwardly obeying the rules, but their actions showed they hadn't taken their beliefs to heart. Just like me, I suppose, but somehow you expect more of them. Jesus attacked them, calling them hypocrites. I guess he saw the Temple as the symbol of all that was wrong with our religion, and that's why he cleared us out. For the priests and the scribes that was the last straw. He had to go. It was either him or them. He didn't stand a chance, really.

JOEL became a Christian – that's what they call those who follow the Way of Jesus. He's really put himself on the line. He says that somehow Jesus' death was part of God's plan. I can't see it that way myself, but he didn't deserve to die. He was a good man.

25
TRICK QUESTIONS

Mark 11.27-12.44

Mark concludes his account of the cleansing of the Temple by saying that the chief priests and the scribes, when they heard what had happened, looked for a way to 'bring about' Jesus' death. They ruled out apprehending him 'for they were afraid of him, because the whole crowd was spellbound at his teaching.'

*Early next morning Jesus returned to Jerusalem. The fig tree that he cursed had withered, a sign perhaps that, like the tree which looks fine with its broad leaves, Jerusalem, which can put on a good religious show, cannot bring forth the fruit of true righteousness. As Jesus walked in the temple court, the chief priests, scribes and elders challenged him about his actions the previous day: 'By what authority are you acting like this? Who gave you authority to act in this way?' **Jonathan**, one of the scribes, recounts what happened.*

I'D been a scribe for a few yeas when I first came across Jesus. As a profession we were critical of him. We were the official interpreters of the law, and our decisions carried as much authority as the law itself. We had status; people looked up to us and respected us. Like the Pharisees, who also took the law seriously, we were conservative in religious matters, and opposed Jesus for overturning tradition and sitting light to the law. Even worse was the subversive purpose that motivated him: he seemed to think that he had been sent to found a new Israel as the true people of God. Did he expect us to abdicate our authority? By the time I actually met him the dispute had become bitter: he condemned us and the Pharisees as blind guides and hypocrites. It was very insulting. Indeed, so bad had things become that the chief priests and the senior scribes were trying to find ways of getting rid of him. They really did want him dead.

But Jesus was popular with the people, and we risked an uprising if we simply arrested him without good cause. And the trouble was that Jesus constantly got the better of us. The senior scribes in particular, found it insufferable that this carpenter's son – from Nazareth of all places – knew the scriptures as well as they did, and spoke with a natural authority that was, I have to say, very impressive. It wasn't surprising that the people were spellbound by his teaching; none of us could hold a candle to him! But after he caused mayhem in the Temple something simply had to be done. We had to find some way of trapping him in his own words, and it had to be done in public, so that it was clear to everyone that there was good cause to arrest him.

It was decided to challenge him directly on the source of his authority. It failed completely! He avoided making any claim of divine authority (which clearly he believed he had) by asking us about John the Baptist: Was his baptism from God or from men? He knew we couldn't answer without compromising our position. If we said 'from God', he'd ask why we didn't believe him; if we said 'from men', we'd risk the wrath of the people who believed that John was indeed a prophet. So, looking utterly pathetic, we answered 'We do not know.' We gave him the perfect excuse not to answer our question. And then to add insult to injury, he told a parable about a vineyard that condemned the priests and scribes as corrupt stewards of God's household. Of course, the people loved it; they got the point all right! So, another question was tried, a crafty one about the poll tax: should we pay it or not? We hadn't learned. He refuted that, and the Saduccees too when they asked him about the resurrection of the dead. He was undermining our authority very effectively. Jesus three: Temple nil!

We walked away with as much dignity as we could muster, but we knew we looked foolish and we felt very angry. As we left we could hear him warning the people: 'Beware of the scribes, who love to walk up and down in long robes and to be greeted respectfully in the street, and to have the chief seats in synagogues and the places of honour at feasts. Those who eat up the property of widows, while for appearance sake they say long prayers, they will receive a sentence all the more severe.'

I'd stopped to listen, out of sight – fortunately my robe was modest and did not give me away. As Jesus was speaking a widow came to make her temple offering. She dropped two tiny coins into the treasury chest, in contrast to the the large offerings of the rich. It was an heaven-sent opportunity, and Jesus seized it. 'Truly, I tell you,' he said, 'this poor widow has given more than all those giving to the treasury; for the others who have given had more than enough, but she, with less than enough, has given all that she had to live on.'

Although I thought something had to be done – after all we weren't all as bad as he said – I was disturbed about the way things were going. The trouble is that when our position is threatened we tend to lash out; it becomes more important to maintain our position than to listen to the criticism and see if it has any merit. Politicians do it all the time, and we, who were meant to be above politics, were behaving just like a bunch of politicians. We scribes are meant to be about seeking the truth, not grubbing around for expedients to defeat our opponents. Some of us thought that on some issues Jesus had a point. We needed to engage with him rather than simply condemn him, but that required moral courage – and wisdom and humility, and right now they were in short supply.

The thing that resonated with me was the way Jesus gave new life to the prophets. As most of our work is with the law, that is with the first five books of the Bible, and we tend not to read the prophets as much as we should. Jesus inspired me to look at them again. In their day they were just as critical as he was of the priests and the powerful in the land. Jesus' story about the vineyard came straight from Isaiah who said Israel was the Lord's vineyard, which he had carefully planted with choice vines and devotedly cared for it, but it had produced wild grapes. It had failed him, so he would tear it down and leave it derelict. *[Isaiah 5.1-7]*

And Jesus' actions in the Temple reminded me of something that Jeremiah had said – actually, Jesus was quoting Jeremiah when he said we'd made the Temple a robbers' cave. There's a passage in Jeremiah that we call the Temple Sermon, and it is swingeing stuff! Like Jesus he didn't mince his words. As well as denouncing wickedness, he actually condemned the system of Temple sacrifices:

> When I brought your forefathers out of Egypt, I gave them
> no instructions or commands about whole-offering or sacrifice.
> What I did command them was this: Obey me, and I shall be
> your God and you will be my people. You must conform to
> my commands if you are to prosper.   *[Jeremiah 7.22–23]*

And when I put a question to Jesus about which was the first of the commandments, Jeremiah's words were in my mind. Jesus replied by quoting the *shema*.* I echoed Jeremiah when I responded: 'Loving God with all your heart, all your under-standing and all your strength, and loving your neighbour as yourself means far more than any whole-offerings or sacrifices.' He replied that I was not far from the Kingdom of God. I may have been one of his critics, but his response was characteristically generous. He may have been bitterly critical, but he wasn't hard-hearted, and his response touched me.

And Jesus was right in his parable of the vineyard. We have been poor stewards of God's household; we have failed to produce the fruits of righteousness, assuming all the time that whatever we did, God would not forsake us. After all, he was *our* God; how could he let us go? But God has, in a way, let us go. He has abandoned his vineyard, as Isaiah prophesied. God's special concern is for the poor, like that widow and her meagre offering, the very people we look down on as inadequate.

I'VE thought about it a lot since then, and it seems to me that we have misunderstood our calling as God's chosen people. To be chosen is to be set apart, but not as an exclusive society. God set us apart to serve, to bring others to God, to share with them what God has shared with us. But we find this hard. It's much easier to keep ourselves to ourselves, than to risk sharing what we've got with others who are different.

Jesus' words as he came to Jerusalem for the last time haunt me: 'O Jerusalem, Jerusalem, city that murders the prophets and stones the messengers sent to her, you do not know the way that makes for peace.' *[Cf. Luke 13.34]* We were completely concerned with politics, avoiding a clash with Rome, but he saw that the real issue was much deeper, a spiritual crisis, and it was on the outcome of that crisis, rather than the present political crisis, that the future of Israel as the people of God depended. We were at a turning point, he said, brought about by his mission. It was clear he thought the present establishment was doomed, and the true people of God would arise from its ruins.

I still feel disturbed about how it all ended. No one, not even sympathetic scribes like me, could ignore his blasphemous claim to be the Messiah, but we forced him into it, and it needn't have ended with his death. He was another prophet sent to us, whom we ignored. If we'd paid more attention to Isaiah and Jeremiah, and the other prophets, perhaps we would have listened to him, and he would still be alive.

26
HOUSE OF SIMON THE LEPER

Mark 14.1-11 + Luke 10.25-37 & 15.11-32*

*For the chief priests the days immediately before the Passover were a busy time, and this year their final preparations had an extra level of anxiety as they tried to work out a way of seizing Jesus and putting him to death. 'It must not be during the festival,' they said, 'or we should have rioting among the people.' Jesus remained at Bethany, where, two days before the festival, he went to supper at the house of Simon the Leper. During the meal a woman came in carrying a bottle of a very costly perfume, pure oil of nard. She poured it over Jesus' head. Some of the guests were indignant, scolding the woman and complaining at the waste: 'The perfume could have been sold for over 300 denarii and the money given to the poor.' Mark does not name the woman; however, John says she was **Mary of Bethany**, the sister of Martha and Lazarus.* She explains her feelings and what her act meant to her:*

BETHANY'S not much of a place, but it's close to Jerusalem, and travellers often stay here on their way to the city. That's how we came to know Jesus – that's me and my sister Martha and our brother Lazarus. When Jesus sent out his disciples on their mission, two of them came to Bethany and stayed at our house. We'd lost our way a bit with religion. We said our prayers, but it wasn't easy for ordinary people like us to keep all the rules; we couldn't see the point of many of them, and we noticed how the rules didn't seem to apply to those at the top; there was always some exception they could take advantage of. So, when Andrew and Thomas came to Bethany with their message that God loved us all, sinners as well as saints, and that his spirit was within us, we wanted to know more. Over several days they taught us as Jesus had taught the crowds in Galilee. It was clear why people hung on his words: the stories were so true to life, and the message so life-giving!

Jesus called his message 'the gospel': the good news. What was really good news for us was God's equal concern for everyone, wherever they came from, whatever their status, and how he longed to forgive.

Thomas told a story about a lawyer who asked Jesus how he could gain eternal life. In response Jesus asked him what the law required. He recited the summary of the Law: 'Love the Lord your God with all your heart, and with all your soul, and with all your strength, and with all your mind; and your neighbour as yourself.' Jesus said that was right: 'Do that and you will live.' But the lawyer persisted, and asked, 'But who is my neighbour?' – being a lawyer, I guess he wanted to know just how far his obligation extended. In reply Jesus told a parable about man attacked by robbers on the way to Jericho, and how he'd been left for dead. A priest and a levite travelling along the road both ignored him, no doubt fearing defilement if they touched a corpse. But a Samaritan – one of those we despise as a perversion of Judaism – a Samaritan had compassion on the victim, and took care of him. 'Who was neighbour to the man who fell into the hands of robbers?' Jesus asked, and the lawyer had to agree that the man's neighbour was the despised Samaritan, and not his fellow Jews. Jesus told him to go and do likewise.*

Jesus spoke of a God whom I could love, but even I could see that his parable challenged our apartness, our separateness from other nations. Jesus said love came before these things; love knew no bounds. For him it was clear: our neighbour was anyone in need; their need alone placed a claim on our love, and trumped all concerns about race, class and religion. If only our teachers could see it this way! If God is the only God, as they say, then his concern must be for everyone. Don't they believe this?

I don't think they do; nor do they seem to think that God's love extends to sinners. Andrew said the scribes and the Pharisees were always complaining about they way Jesus reached out to sinners. 'Do you remember that occasion,' he asked Thomas, 'when they said among themselves, "This fellow welcomes sinners and eats with them."?' 'Yes, I do,' Thomas replied, smiling, and told us another parable that Jesus had told in response.* A man had two sons. The elder was dutiful; he stayed at home and looked after the farm. The younger was a wastrel. He took his inheritance, left home and went to a far country where he lost it all in dissolute living. He was reduced to looking after the pigs. In his misery he realised that his father's servants were far better treated. He realised he had forfeited his status as a son; he resolved to go home and ask to become a servant. But his father would have none of it. When his son's return was reported to him, he ran to meet him, even though he was a long way off, flung his arms round him and kissed him. And a great party was held. That, said Thomas, was how Jesus saw God rejoicing over those who repent and turn to him: 'There is greater joy in heaven over one sinner who repents than over ninety-nine people who do not need to repent.'

'What about the other son,' Lazarus asked, 'what did he feel about it?'

'I should think he felt resentful,' Martha spoke with feeling. 'I know what it's like to do all the work and be taken for granted. I bet he didn't get a party!'

'Well, no, he didn't,' Thomas replied carefully, 'but his father loved him just as dearly as his younger brother. He said to him, "You are always with me, and everything I have is yours. How could we fail to celebrate this happy day? You brother here was dead and has come back to life; he was lost and has been found."'

I knew how he felt. In our village there were some parents who were beside themselves with joy when their wayward son came home. It can be hard being the eldest like Martha. We talked about it afterwards and she softened. We all found Jesus' picture of God so compelling: not remote and judgemental, but close and forgiving – even running towards us when we turn to him. What Thomas and Andrew said rang true, and we also became disciples.

IT was a bit odd really, because the three of us didn't often agree, but we were united as followers of Jesus. It wasn't long before we met him, and our lives were really turned around! And we began to wonder just who he was: could he be the Messiah? At first I wasn't sure, but the conviction gradually grew on me that he must be the one. There was just something about him. He had an amazing natural authority. He touched your heart in a way no one else did. When you were with him you could feel the love of God. He really brought good news to the poor, one of the things that Isaiah had said the Messiah would do. With Jesus we knew we were especially beloved by God, just as the prophets had said. He gave sight to the blind and hearing to the deaf; the lame could walk and lepers were cleansed. We actually knew one of the lepers that he'd healed: Simon who lives not far from us in Bethany.

It was easy to understand why the priests and the others in Jerusalem took against him: he was the real thing, and they were not. He really knew God; they only knew about God. Jerusalem was rife with rumours that the priests wanted to do away with him. He knew it too. We warned him against going there, but he was determined. 'The Son of Man,' he said, 'will be handed over to the chief priests and the scribes; they will condemn him to death and hand him over to the Gentiles. He will be mocked and spat upon, and flogged and killed; and three days afterwards, he will rise again.' He spoke of it as a destiny that he couldn't avoid. I didn't really understand, especially when he spoke about rising again, but I knew something dreadful was going to happen to him, and that's why, when he came to supper at Simon's house, I wanted to be near him.

We'd been to Simon's house many times so I knew my way around. All sorts of things were going through my head, but one thought kept coming back to me: 'Messiah' means 'anointed one'. I know it sounds crazy, but I felt I was being sent to anoint him. I had to show them who Jesus was: Simon, his guests, the disciples, everyone … the whole world really. It would be just like the story of David who was anointed to be king of Israel. Samuel poured oil over his head, precious oil, that smelled sweet and carried with it the blessings of God and the gift of his spirit.

After we got to know Simon, I looked after his mother and cared for her as she died. He was very grateful and gave me the most precious thing I possess, a flask of Oil of Nard – it must have cost a fortune! But Jesus was more precious to me; nothing was too good for him; I would use my Oil of Nard to anoint him.

Well, I did. I expected the other guests to understand, but they didn't. A chorus of criticism broke out: 'Why was this not sold and the money given to the poor?' I felt humiliated. But Jesus understood what I had done. He told them to leave me alone. He said I'd done a fine thing for him: 'You have the poor among you always, and you can help them whenever you like; but you will not always have me. She has done what lay in her power; she has anointed my body in anticipation of my burial.' He knew what was in my heart, and he accepted it. But I had to leave. My heart was so full; I sat outside Simon's house and wept.

THINKING about it afterwards, I remembered Jesus had said something else: that wherever the gospel is proclaimed throughout the world, what I had done would be told as my memorial. I hope so. It was my way of saying how much I loved him, and how much he meant to me. Simon and the others must have spoken about what I did because people have talked to me about it, people I hardly know. I do seem to have become part of the story of Jesus.

I remembered also what Jesus said about us always having the poor but not always having him. This was a bit surprising given God's special concern for the poor that was so close to Jesus' heart. I talked about it with Lazarus. He'd also been surprised, but as he thought about it, he'd realised that deep down religion is about our relationship with God, about who we are, not about what we do, and this came first, even before our concern for the poor. When we get our relationship with God right, we will get our other relationships right, and the poor will be cared for. Through us they will know God's generous love. That made sense to me. I suppose that as I poured the oil over Jesus, giving him the best that I had, he'd seen in my action a reflection of God's overflowing generosity to us. I think that's what Jesus wanted: generous and loving hearts. That love was missing in the Temple; you didn't hear much about it in what the priests taught us about God.

I was a bit amazed at all this. I only did what my heart told me to do. But I guess not everyone is in touch with their heart, and they tend to keep their acts of gratitude for their family and friends, and those they want to impress, rather than for God. I suppose God hasn't touched their lives in the way that Jesus touched mine.

He died for a lack of love.

27
UPPER ROOM

Mark 14.12-31

*On the evening of the next day events began to move more swiftly. It was the day on which the Passover was celebrated, and Jesus had made arrangements to use 'a large upstairs room' (the owner of which is not named) to eat the celebratory meal with his disciples. Judas Iscariot, one of the twelve, had by then decided to betray Jesus, and had been to the chief priests. They had promised him money, and he began to look for an opportune time. Meanwhile Jesus sent two disciples to prepare the meal. One of them, **Philip**, sets the scene:* *

JESUS may not have been popular with the authorities, but he had many friends among the ordinary people – friends who were willing to take risks for him. So, when James and I – young James, as we called him, not big James, the brother of John – were asked to go and prepare for the Passover meal, it was to the house of a friend that we went. We all had that dreadful sinking feeling because the authorities were closing in on Jesus. It was too risky for them to arrest him by day, so we expected them to try and take him by night. It was likely to be that very night, and we needed a safe house where we could celebrate the Passover undisturbed.

The precautions were elaborate. Jesus sent us, rather than two of the better-known disciples, to get things ready. As we entered the city he said we would meet a man carrying a water jar. He stood out more than you might think, as water jars are usually carried by women, not men. He was half-hidden in the shadows; we almost missed him. He led us to a house in a remote part of the city. The entrance was more or less concealed behind some trees in the courtyard. We needed a guide; we'd never have found it otherwise. It must have belonged to someone that Jesus knew, someone he'd helped and who wanted to repay the debt. Over the years we realised Jesus had lots of contacts with people unknown to us. We didn't know who he was, and thought it best not to ask. If you don't know, you can't tell.

The house was surprisingly spacious, with a large upstairs room which our unknown host had already set out. We'd brought the food with us and we began to get it ready.

Passover is quite an elaborate meal, full of ritual and symbolism. James and I talked about it as we prepared the food: the lamb, the bitter herbs, the unleavened bread and the wine. Originally, it was eaten standing, 'in urgent haste' as it says in the scriptures, but now we sit down – actually, we recline on couches, like the Romans, a sign that we're free-born, no longer slaves. And, of course, that's why we celebrate it. We remember God's great act of deliverance when he rescued us from slavery in Egypt and brought us to freedom in the Promised Land. It was the Exodus that transformed the Israelites from a rabble of slaves into a nation. We became the People of God, and God bound us to him and him to us in a Covenant: he would be our God and we would be his people. The Covenant is basic to what it means to be a Jew.

All this was in our minds – we'd done it so many times and with joy in our hearts, but on that day it was hard to be joyful, and darker thoughts clouded our minds. Jesus had taught us that Israel had failed to understand the Covenant properly, and hadn't lived up to its terms. We had thought the covenant gave us a privileged position, separating us from the other nations, but in truth, he said, we were meant to become their servant, leading them to God. And the laws of the Covenant had been so elaborated in so many detailed rules, that we'd lost sight of its basic purpose.

Jesus said that through him, God was making a New Covenant with his people, as the prophets had foretold, and that we, the twelve, were the foundation of the new Israel. Just as the old covenant had been sealed with the blood of the passover lambs, so the new covenant would be sealed by the shedding of his blood.

It was too much to take in. We didn't want to go where Jesus was leading. We were scared. It all felt very dark.

James, son of Alphaeus, takes up the story.*

NONE of us will ever forget that meal. It was the last time we were all together with Jesus. As we'd travelled with him he'd often spoken about being handed over to the chief priests and being put to death. He spoke of it as something he had to do, rather than something that would be done to him. We didn't want to think about it, but it was always there in the background, in the back of our minds, and when he turned towards Jerusalem, we knew the time had come. But when we arrived he wasn't arrested, as we'd expected. In fact the priests were wary of him, and seemed afraid to act. But then, as Philip said, we realised they would come at night, out of sight of the crowds.

But how would they know where he was? The meal had hardly begun when Jesus provided the answer: one of us would betray him. I thought he meant that someone would make a mistake and give the game away; but no, he was talking about a deliberate act of betrayal. One of us around the table had turned against him; he would do it. We couldn't believe it; we all protested, 'Surely, you don't mean me?' But we weren't as strong as we thought we were. When things were going well we were happy to stand by him, but I think we all knew in our hearts that under pressure it would be a different story. I think Jesus knew it would be Judas. We didn't know he'd already been to the priests and arranged it. So, it wasn't someone caving in under pressure, but a deliberate act as Jesus had said. I could never work out why he did it, and I thought I knew him well.

There was so much going on in my mind, it was hard to stay focussed on the Passover until Jesus changed the ritual. He added some words when broke the bread, and then again when he passed round the cup of blessing. He said the bread was his body, and the cup was his blood, the blood of the covenant, shed for many. This was it, the new covenant he had spoken about; this was something we had to remember. This meal wasn't just a Passover supper but something new, and as we ate the bread and drank from the cup we had a new sense of fellowship, with him and with each other. They say to share a loaf is to share each other's blessing, and to share a cup is to share each other's fate. Well, that's what we were doing. We were being bound together with Jesus so that we shared his blessing in order to continue his work and share his fate.

It was an ending, but it was also a new beginning. And it was heart-rending. Jesus was deeply moved. Knowing he was to be betrayed – and the dreadful fate that awaited him – he said in deep anguish of spirit that he would not drink again from the fruit of the vine until he drank it anew in the kingdom of God. It wasn't until sometime afterwards that I realised just what he meant. His death was the turning point; God's new age was about to begin.

So, with a terrible sense of foreboding we sang the Passover hymn and went out. He said we'd all desert him. Peter protested that whatever the rest of us did, *he* would *never* lose faith. But Jesus knew him – and us – better. When Judas came with the soldiers, he was on his own.

28

GETHSEMANE

Mark 14.32-52 + Luke 6.6-11

*After the Passover supper Jesus led the disciples to the Mount of Olives where there was a garden. It is clear Both Luke and John say Jesus went there often. Luke says that after the supper he made his way there 'as usual' (Luke 22.39); John says it was known to Judas 'because Jesus had often met there with his disciples' (John 18.2). The garden was a secluded place away from the crowds, and it was to there that Judas led the temple police. In his account of the betrayal and arrest of Jesus, Mark adds the incident of the young man, dressed only in a loincloth, who ran away naked. Tradition has it that the young man was **Mark** himself, who tells what happened:*

My mother knew Jesus. She was called Mary like his mother. We lived in Jerusalem, and after he died his followers used to meet in our house. I was much younger in those days, and never really talked to Jesus, though I liked to be around when he came. There was something about him – he wasn't like the others – something within him shone out; it touched you and made you feel special. Sometimes I would go with my mother to hear him speak. On one occasion, there'd been a row among his disciples about who was the greatest, and Jesus had taken a young child and put his arm round him, and said that those who wanted to be great must be willing to serve the least, like that child. That stayed with me. As I said, Jesus wasn't like other men.

Although crowds gathered wherever he went, I realised Jesus wasn't popular with everyone, above all the authorities. There were some bitter arguments with those I'd been taught to respect and look up to: the scribes and the Pharisees, and the priests. There was one occasion – I think I was eleven – when I was sitting with my mother in the synagogue and Jesus was there. He saw a man whose right arm was withered. He knew they were watching him. He asked the man to come forward, which he did. You could have heard a pin drop, it was so tense. He looked at the scribes, 'I put this question to you: is it permitted to do good or to do evil on the sabbath, to save life or to destroy it?' He looked round at the whole assembly, holding us with his gaze. No one answered. The atmosphere was charged, and I seized my mother's hand. Then, turning to the man, Jesus said quite simply, 'Stretch out your arm.' He did so, and it was restored. You should have seen the look on the man's face! Everyone gasped. The scribes looked furious. I knew well by then how the law circumscribed our lives. You weren't meant to do work on the sabbath, and healing was work. I was beginning to get a sense of the nice distinctions the rabbis and scribes used when applying the law. I knew about wriggle-words from arguing with my mother, but it was evident, even to me, that Jesus wasn't interested in fine distinctions and special pleading; he went straight to the heart of the matter.

He confronted danger; he seemed unafraid; but I overheard talk among his disciples about the authorities wanting to arrest him. I'd heard that Jesus believed his destiny was to go to Jerusalem where he would die and rise again. No one understood what he meant, but increasingly it felt as though things were coming to a climax. His disciples were afraid, not just for him, but for themselves as well. If they killed him, what would their fate be?

They came by night.

A FRIEND who had a house near ours let Jesus use it for the Passover. After the meal I followed as Jesus led the disciples through the narrow streets and alleys, down the steep hill of the Kidron valley, across the stream, and up the other side to Gethsemane, where there's a lovely peaceful garden. It was one of the places where Jesus had rested before. In the middle of the garden is a large rock.

Everyone was tired, not just physically, but also emotionally wrung out. Jesus told them to find a place to sit while he prayed. He asked Peter and James and John to come with him. I crept closer; sleep had overtaken the others and they didn't notice me. I was apprehensive, and what happened next really scared me. Jesus, who had always seemed so in control, seemed now to be in despair. He said to the three of them, 'My heart is ready to break with grief, stop here and stay awake.' As they sat down he went forward to the rock, and threw himself on the ground. I'll never forget his words: 'Abba, father, all things are possible to you; take this cup from me. ' And then he added, 'Yet not my will but yours.'

This wasn't the Jesus who had amazed the people; who challenged the rulers; who taught us that God is a loving father whom we could trust. Now, kneeling against that rock, his confidence and trust seemed to have deserted him as the reality of what was about to happen to him overwhelmed him. It was too much, even for him. Even though a young lad, I knew horror and anguish when I saw it. This was, I learned later, the cost of reconciliation, the cost of what Jesus came to do. And he was alone. The three whom he took with him for support fell asleep. The spirit may be willing, but the flesh is weak, and we were men of flesh.

Then we heard a noise; someone was coming. Jesus rose; his authority returned; Judas entered the garden. 'Enough!' Jesus said, 'The hour has come. The Son of Man is betrayed into the hands of sinners. Up, let us go! The traitor is upon us.' Judas wasn't alone; with him was a large crowd armed with swords and cudgels. What were they expecting, armed resistance – from us? Well, someone did have a sword, and used it. But Jesus was a man of peace and his disciples didn't carry weapons, he told the man sharply to put his sword away. I realise now that the force was far too big for what they had to do; clearly they thought of Jesus not as a trouble-maker, but as an enemy of the state.

What happened next sickened me. Judas went up to Jesus, and kissed him. I remember Jesus speaking about those who preferred darkness to light because their deeds were evil; well, here they were, the forces of evil, and Judas was leading them. Jesus was betrayed by a kiss, that most intimate sign of friendship. As I learned then, evil always seeks to mask its true nature, and in Gethsemane betrayal wore the mask of love.

It's easy to pile all the blame on Judas. Everyone else, seeing what had happened, turned and fled, me included. We were no better. Someone tried to grab me, and caught my loincloth. It was all that I had on, but I let it go. To be seen naked is shameful; but I was so scared for myself, I was prepared to risk public humiliation rather than stay close to Jesus.

The shame has never left me.

29
House of Caiaphas

Mark 14.53-72

*From Gethsemane Jesus was taken under guard to the house of Caiaphas, the High Priest, where the chief priests, elders and scribes were assembling. **Peter** had enough courage to follow at a distance, going right into the High Priest's courtyard, where he sat among the attendants and warmed himself by the fire. He tells what happened:*

I RAN away, like the others – not out of the garden, but into the trees, out of sight. I recognised some of the guards from Caiaphas' house and guessed they would be taking him there – that's where they took people for what they called 'questioning', but everyone knew that it was worse than that, far worse. There was a punishment room in the basement where those who didn't give the right answers were given a bit of help remembering. I was scared, but I had to go there. I'd run away in the garden, but I wanted to keep faith. I had to go; but I kept my distance.

The house is some way from Gethsemane, down the valley, and up the other side, and then into the city and over to the west side. I saw them take Jesus into the house, and at the same time lots of people were arriving, even though it was the middle of the night. I recognised some of them: Annas, Nathaniel, Nicodemus and other members of the High Council. I feared the worst. They were losing no time, clearly this had all been planned.

There was a fire in the courtyard; some of the servants were warming themselves. They let me join them. All the talk was about Jesus, and what was going to happen to him. I recognised one of them who had hung around and listened to Jesus when he had taught in the Temple, but he had changed sides. Now that he could see how things were going to work out, he was joining in the cruel jokes about what they'd do to him if they had the chance.

I kept quiet.

As we sat there, the sound of shouting and angry voices came from the house. We didn't know exactly what was going on, but it wasn't long before it leaked out. There was no pretence of justice; they wanted to get him, and it seems it didn't matter how, so long as they could find some pretext to justify his execution. It was unbelievable. We are the nation founded by Moses; through him God gave us the Law. We prided ourselves on our superior standards, our moral superiority; and now here were our leaders ignoring the law, listening to wicked lies invented by low dogs who'd do anything for money, grubbing around for evidence to allow them to justify the 'guilty' verdict they had already passed on him. This was what you expected of an Assyrian tyrant, not the High Priests of Israel, the leaders of the People of God.

Although many gave evidence, it wasn't credible; a proper court would have rejected it out of hand. Caiaphas tried to bully Jesus into condemning himself, but he remained silent. Eventually, Caiaphas asked him outright, 'Are you the Messiah, the Son of the Blessed One?' Jesus answered 'I am.' In the end he said the very thing he had been so careful to avoid saying in public, and that sealed his fate. They had their evidence.

And then it was my turn.

IN the courtyard, round the fire, I was put on trial. I also was asked a direct question about who I was, but   rather than admit the truth, I lied. One of the servant girls had seen me with Jesus, and someone else recognised my Galilean accent. Three times they accused me of being 'one of them', and three times I denied it. I was gripped by fear. It was all too threatening, too sudden; I couldn't bear the thought of pain and torture; my faith failed me.

At the end of the supper I'd said that even if I had to die with Jesus, I would never disown him. I wanted to believe it, but I wasn't ready to be put to the test. It was an empty boast. And at that moment the cock crowed for the second time. It was just as Jesus had said: 'Peter, before the cock crows twice, you will disown me three times.' I ran out of the courtyard and burst into tears. They all saw it; they all knew the truth.

SOME time afterwards I began to understand it all a bit more clearly. The priests weren't wicked men, but they were powerful men. They were convinced they were right, and they thought they were acting in the national interest, but they also knew their position was threatened. These are ideal conditions for evil to take root. Our lower nature comes to the aid of our good intentions, and we come to think that the end justifies the means.

Jesus didn't just challenge the priests spiritually; he threatened the very foundations of their authority, and he had strong popular support. Like all leaders, the priests considered the national interest and their personal interest to be identical: to overthrow the established order would be a disaster for the nation. Jesus had to go.

And what of me? Jesus said that anyone who wanted to be a follower of his must renounce self; he must take up his cross and follow him. 'Whoever wants to save his life will lose it, but whoever loses his life for my sake and for the gospel's will save it.' It sounded so heroic, and it made sense in my head – but my heart was elsewhere. I was too attached to the life I knew, to my home and my possessions, and to the good opinion of my friends. In my own way, I was like the priests. I felt threatened; too much was being asked of me; too much was at stake; I wasn't ready to give it all up. And so I deserted him, and left him alone to his fate.

30
PRAETORIUM

Mark 15.1-15

*Getting evidence to convict Jesus of heresy was a preliminary to getting him executed. Only the Romans, the occupying power, could impose the death penalty, and so the chief priests had to work out how they could do this. After they condemned Jesus (in the early morning), the next part of their plan was put into effect, and they brought Jesus before Pontius Pilate, the Roman Governor. They must have prepared the way, because Pilate was ready to hear the case at an early hour, as **Gaius Flavius**, Pilate's secretary, relates:*

'WE'RE going to Judea,' Pilate announced. I'd worked for him for two years; I had hoped we might be posted to Alexandria, or Corinth, somewhere with a bit of life, not Judea! Pilate had tried hard to avoid it, but the Emperor was adamant: Pilate was the man for the job – the job being dealing with the Jews. We Romans found them difficult, they disputed everything, and weren't at all pragmatic in the Roman way. It was all tied up with their incomprehensible religion; their laws; and their sense of destiny as the chosen people of God. Well, their god was welcome to them!

Pilate wasn't an easy man to work for, and his reputation for harshness may have been why he was sent to Judea. We were there for ten years, and it was about four years after we arrived that Jesus first came on the scene. We'd heard about him, but no more than that, until he came to Jerusalem three years later. It was at the Passover – always a tense time for us with so many people crowding into the city and a real risk of serious disorder. The day before the festival, the High Priest, Caiaphas, had come to us in a fury. Jesus had caused serious damage and disruption in the Temple. They hadn't been able to arrest him at the time, but they were going to arrest him that night. It was a serious matter; he was trying to overthrow the state, and because of the Passover, they wanted the case dealt with as early as possible the next day. A bit to my surprise, Pilate agreed, but then he had to work with priests, and doing Caiaphas a favour now might be useful if he wanted something from him in the future.

So, we were up and ready very early in the morning when they came with Jesus.

Of course, it was a religious dispute. But they dressed it up as treason, saying Jesus had claimed to be king, and they demanded he be put to death. It was obvious to us both this was a trumped-up charge. His years as governor had done nothing to lessen Pilate's contemptuous attitude towards the priests and their religion, and his feelings showed. Jesus had been beaten by Caiaphas' men and was a pathetic figure. Pilate looked at him and said, '*You* ... are the king of the Jews? ' Calling him 'King of the Jews' was an expression of contempt, but Jesus didn't rise to the insult, instead he replied, 'The words are yours,' and that was all he said. Even when the priests pressed their case, to our astonishment, he said nothing.

It was clear he'd done nothing that deserved death; the allegation that he claimed to be king was laughable, and there was nothing else in their accusations that the priests could not have dealt with themselves. But things began to look ugly. A crowd had gathered outside the Praetorium, and they were shouting for Jesus to be crucified. There was a real risk of a riot. Pilate withdrew and asked my advice. I suggested he release Jesus under the Passover amnesty. The problem was that the people chose who should be released, so he had to ask them. The priests had got a crowd together; they rejected the releasing Jesus, demanding instead the release of a notorious criminal called Barabbas. It was all going badly wrong. A power struggle with the priests was one thing, a power struggle with the people quite another, and it was clear they saw an opportunity to get even with the hated occupying power. What was one man's life balanced against the deaths, damage and destruction a riot would unleash? The priests and the people got their way; Pilate handed Jesus over to be crucified.

IN the end it's pragmatism, not justice, that decides these things. You can't be too scrupulous. Politics is the art of the possible, not of the moral. And generally the people you're dealing with are more concerned with preserving their power and status than they are with justice or morality. Balancing powerful competing interests needs guile, and any good intentions you may have get lost.

But, even so, I wasn't happy with what we did that day. We averted a riot, but we handed Caiaphas a triumph; justice was defeated, the governor's authority was weakened, and an innocent man was sacrificed. He wasn't the first and he won't be the last.

Romans as well as Jews know about sacrifice. The price of wrongdoing has to be paid to the gods, and Jesus of Nazareth was that price. He was sacrificed to preserve the peace – the peace that was threatened by our vanity and ambition, by our compromises and our pragmatism.

31
GOLGOTHA

Mark 15.16-39

*Pilate handed Jesus over to be crucified, and he was taken in hand by the soldiers. It was the Roman practice to beat prisoners before they were crucified in order to weaken their resistance; with Jesus they also mocked and insulted him. From the Praetorium Jesus is led to Golgotha, which, Mark says means 'Place of a Skull' where he was crucified. The centurion, **Longinus**, relates what happened.*

I DIDN'T join the army to deal with petty criminals. If you're a soldier, killing people is what you have to do, but in battle you're also putting your own life at risk. There's an honour in soldiering, but there's no risk, no honour in doing executions. None of us liked doing them, and I think that's why we took it out on those who were condemned. They got our anger at having to do others' dirty work.

And we could be rough. Well ... if the prisoner was going to die anyway, he was as good as dead when he was handed over to us. He'd forfeited his right to be treated as a human being ... not much better than rubbish. We had a good time with Jesus. We softened him up a bit, then dressed him in purple like a king, put a crown of thorns on his head, and bowed down to him in mock homage. I suppose it was cruel, but it prepared him for the walk to Golgotha, just outside the city wall. It's a long way through the narrow, winding alleys of Jerusalem. And if they've still got any fight left, it's beaten out of them on the journey. It's so narrow that people are right up against you, close enough to hit the prisoner, trip him up and spit upon him. And they did. Like most, Jesus needed help. We grabbed someone in the crowd – he stood out because of his dark skin – and he got his share of the abuse too. Poor sod!

Crucifixion is a terrible way to die. We used to nail them to the cross, but there was blood everywhere, and it didn't always work. The nails often split the bone and lost their grip, so now we tie them on with rope. And then we haul them up, fix the cross-bar to the post, and leave them hanging. It's not a pretty sight; you need a strong stomach.

We put a sign over him: *The King of the Jews.*

We had to hang around until they were dead, partly to make sure no one came and cut them down, and partly to keep the crowds away. As it was, people came up and jeered, even the chief priests and the scribes. It was all to do with their religion: 'He saved others,' they said, 'but he cannot save himself. Let the Messiah, the king of Israel, come from down from the cross. If we see that, we shall believe.' Well, that seemed unlikely! The way the Jewish leaders joined in the mockery sickened even me. We soldiers are a rough lot, but these were civilised, learned men behaving just like us.

Of course, he didn't come down, we'd made sure of that, but something did happen. While he was hanging there everything went dark, as though the gods were angry. And he gave a dark cry, 'My God, my God, why have you forsaken me?' I can tell you it was eerie, and he looked utterly forsaken. Whatever he'd expected didn't happen. All the fight had gone out of him. After three hours, he gave a loud cry and died.

I'd had enough: enough of standing around, enough of the spite of the crowd, enough of the darkness, enough of religion. Some women were there at the end too. They were completely crushed. I think they thought he was divine. Well, he didn't die like a god. As I said to Sabinus, who'd seen it all too, 'Don't tell me *this* man was the Son of God?'*

And then the darkness lifted.

32

SEPULCHRE

Mark 15.40-47

Mark says that by the time Jesus died, evening had come. Joseph of Arimathea, 'a respected member of the Council who looked forward to the kingdom of God,' asked Pilate for the body of Jesus for burial. Pilate was surprised that Jesus had died so quickly (crucifixion was normally a long, excruciatingly painful death), and having ascertained from Longinus that he was indeed dead, gave Joseph leave to bury him. **Joseph of Arimathea** *was one of the leaders of Israel sympathetic to Jesus, as he explains:*

IT was a black day, the worst I can remember, and there were black deeds; too many, and too awful. I was almost alone among the High Council in my regard for Jesus. He was a prophet, not afraid to speak a few home truths that we needed to hear, just like Isaiah and Jeremiah. Jonathan, the scribe, felt the same; Nicodemus too, I think, and that was it. We were a small minority, and, although respected, in practice our views were easily ignored by the majority. We could have resigned, but we felt it was important to be there, to represent those who felt like us. There were many who were unhappy with the way things were going in Israel, and who wanted to keep the prophetic tradition alive. But if we wanted to keep our position on the council and have our views heard, we could not be too open in our support for Jesus. I was, I suppose, a secret disciple.

The decision to execute Jesus sickened me. The evidence so flimsy; the outcome predetermined. If only he had kept silent... but then that would have been to deny himself. I was deeply disturbed. Perhaps I could have done more, but the chance had come and gone, and now he was dead, and our hopes had died with him. The least I could do was to give him a proper burial, so I went to Pilate and asked for his body. I had arranged to buy a new tomb; we took down his disfigured, mutilated body, now cold and limp, wrapped him in a shroud, carried him to the tomb, and laid him there.

I HAD seen Jesus from the back of the crowd but had never been close to him; now I held him in my arms. And as I held the body of Jesus, I asked myself, what was I holding? Was this indeed the Son of God? What was the meaning of his death? It took a long time – many years – before I had an answer.

We Jews have a very demanding picture of God. So had Jesus, but he saw that the demands were the demands of love, not wrath. God was just but he was also merciful. Isaiah had seen this too. When Israel had been conquered by Babylon, we believed God had punished us for our wrongdoing. Well, he had punished us, but Isaiah saw he had also provided a way back into his fellowship by taking the burden of our wrong-doing upon himself. This resonated with my own experience.

There were often serious divisions in the High Council; people fell out, and bringing them together again required a peace-maker. I had often been in this rôle. It's exhausting, lonely, and painful work. You have to give of yourself in building the bridge of reconciliation. Peace-making involves self-sacrifice; you have to put yourself on the line; you have to accept that you will be hurt as you bear the anger and the lack of trust. What is true for the sons of men is so much more true of the Son of God. Isaiah pictured the servant of God who did this sacrificial, reconciling work. He saw the servant disfigured by suffering, despised and rejected, 'an object from which people turn away their eyes.' But, said Isaiah, 'he was pierced for our transgressions, crushed for our iniquities ... by his wounds we are healed ... the Lord laid on him the guilt of us all.' *[Isaiah 53.3-6]* As I held in my arms the ruined remains of Jesus, I held the world's ransom, the price of our reconciliation with God.

Years later, Paul of Tarsus, whom I'd met once, said that 'God was in Christ reconciling the world to himself, no longer holding people's misdeeds against them.' *[2 Corinthians 5.19]* God did not come to the aid of Jesus on the cross, because in Jesus God himself was on the cross. And there he bore my sins, my weaknesses, my failure to stand up for him. He bore the sins of the disciples who had deserted him; the sins of the priests; of Pilate; the people who had condemned him, and of the soldiers who killed him. He was the peace-maker. He built the bridge of reconciliation that no-one else could build.

The God of love hung on the cross, and that Friday evening I held his Son in my arms. As the sun went down and we laid him to rest, he took our sins to the grave.

33
New Dawn

Mark 16.1–8a

The last thing the followers of Jesus expected after his execution was that he would rise from the dead. Several times in his story Mark has said that Jesus spoke of his death and predicted his resurrection but the disciples had not understood what he meant. This is hardly surprising: the resurrection was something completely beyond human experience. So, when the Sabbath was over, three women, Mary of Magdala, Mary the mother of James, and Salome, went to the tomb as early as they could, just after sunrise, to perform the last rites for Jesus, the anointing of his body. **Mary of Magdala** *concludes the story.**

I WAS almost the same age as Jesus, and he was the first of my friends to die. But he was so much more than a friend. He'd touched my life in a way that no one else had ever done. He'd literally turned my life around – I was a new person – I owed him everything. And then they'd taken him and crucified him. It was the cruellest thing they could have done. It's an appalling way to die. We were numb with grief. I stayed near him as he hung on the cross, with Mary his mother and my friends Mary, the mother of James, and Salome. The three of us had followed him in Galilee, caring for him, and as we watched, his life slowly ebbed away.

When it was all over, we wondered what would happen to him. Where would he be buried? Who would do it? As we waited, two men appeared with a grave-cloth and a ladder. I recognised one of them as Joseph of Arimathea. He came across and spoke to us. He told Mary that he'd asked Pilate for permission to take Jesus down from the cross and bury him, and Pilate had agreed. She looked so relieved – and grateful for this act of love and compassion after so much cruelty. They took him down, wrapped him in a grave cloth, and carried him away. We followed and saw the tomb where they laid him. It was almost the Sabbath, so there was no time to anoint him. We'd have to come back when the Sabbath was over.

I'LL never forget that Sabbath. It was the longest, the bleakest day of my life. How we endured it I do not know. God must have given us strength. We couldn't sleep. We were up and ready long before dawn … just waiting. As soon as dawn broke, we set out with the oils for anointing. We were worried about how we would roll away the stone from the entrance to the tomb, could three women manage it? And then, as we got closer, we saw that it had been rolled away. We panicked, our hearts beating so fast, and began to run. Questions raced through our minds: Who had moved the stone? Had someone stolen the body? Had the priests taken him away? It was just too awful; a final humiliation. And when we looked into the tomb our worst fears were confirmed. He wasn't there.

We stood there immobile, beside ourselves with grief, tears were streaming down our faces, we could hardly see … and then … we saw him! We thought it was him, but no, it was a young man, in a white robe. The tomb gradually filled with light. We just stood there, trembling, speechless. He could see the state we were in and he said gently, 'Don't be alarmed. You're looking for Jesus of Nazareth, who was crucified. He has been raised; he's not here.' He pointed to the place where they'd laid him. And then he said that Jesus was going on ahead of us into Galilee, where we would meet him. He said we must tell Peter and the disciples. We stood there trembling with fright and amazement, and then, all three of us turned and ran for our lives. We were in such a state that if we'd seen the others we wouldn't have known what to say. But we didn't see anyone, and we said nothing.

We found somewhere to sit, and just sat in silence. More questions tumbled through our minds: Who was that young man in white? And what did he mean – Jesus had been raised? And then we began to talk. Salome said it didn't look as if anything violent had happened. The stone wasn't broken, the tomb was undisturbed, and the young man had been ... well ... angelic ... calm and reassuring. And then it dawned on us: Jesus had said that this is what would happen. He would be put to death and on the third day he would be raised. And this was the third day...

We were in a state of shock. This wasn't what we were expecting. None of us had understood what Jesus had said about being raised. We thought his death was the end, that the forces of evil had triumphed ... but now ... we weren't so sure. We had a glimmer of hope. Jesus had raised people from death – we'd been there when he raised Jairus' daughter – and now had he also been raised? We couldn't take it in. What had happened on that Sabbath while we waited in grief and despair?

There was no answer, no one knew; and even to this day no one knows. All we knew was that Jesus was alive. And whatever had happened, it was God who had made it happen. Salome said it was a mystery.

'A mystery?' I asked.

'Yes,' she said, 'a mystery – like love – something you can experience but which you can't really explain. I think what happened was a great act of love which came from God himself: something quite beyond our human knowing, but not beyond our human experience.'

I knew what she meant. But there were so many questions. It wasn't quite like Jairus' daughter who had been restored to an earthly life. Jesus wasn't with us; there was no body in the tomb; so where was he now?

The truth took time to dawn on us. The only way we could explain it was that Jesus seemed now to be in a new order of existence, beyond the limits of time and space, like God himself. At first we were scared, but gradually we got bolder. Peter and the others lost their fear and literally became new men, now defying the priests rather than running away. And many Gentiles became believers, like Cornelius in Caesarea.* The love of God reached beyond Israel to everyone, just as Jesus had said. And in his name people were healed and forgiven, and given new hope.

I STILL look back on it and can hardly believe it. How our lives had changed! We'd been overwhelmed with grief and despair as we went to the tomb ... frightened and dumbfounded as we ran away ... and now we were beside ourselves with joy! In one of the psalms it says, 'I will change your mourning into dancing, and clothe you with joy.' [Psalm 30.11] And that's what had happened. God's joy was ours! We were filled with hope; God's new day had dawned!

It all felt wonderful, but what was its meaning? I believe that raising Jesus was God's sign to us that all that Jesus said and did was true. His words are God's words; his values are God's values; his concern for the poor and the outcast is God's concern; and his forgiveness is God's forgiveness. Most of all God raising Jesus says that he is a loving father, and we can trust him with our lives.

Jesus called himself the 'Son of Man'; truly, he was the Son of God.

NOTES

3   *1.* There are no independent historical records supporting the Biblical stories before the seventh century BCE. While the stories of Abraham, Moses and the other patriarchs are unlikely to be fictitious, it is impossible to know what basis they have in fact.

2. It is common these days to use inclusive language in Christian writing, a convention which I generally follow, but sometimes this results in awkward or unnatural formulations, like the term 'Godself', and so sometimes I use the traditional male pronoun. This use is not to be understood as ascribing gender to God. God is beyond gender; as it says in *Genesis*, both male and female are created in the image of God *(Genesis 1.27-28)* in whom all our differences are held in harmony.

4   The divine name 'Yahweh' was never uttered; instead God was referred to reverentially as 'the Lord'. In texts, Yahweh was abbreviated to YHWH, usually rendered in English in small capitals: LORD, and I have followed this convention.

5   In ancient cultures a change of name often indicated a change of destiny. In the same way Jacob is renamed Israel, Simon became Peter, and Saul became Paul.

7   The plagues are described in *Exodus 6.28-12.36*. The Biblical account reflects a primitive understanding of God as one who would inflict appalling suffering on innocent people in order to punish their ruler for his obduracy. Needless to say, this under-standing of God is light years away from the God of love revealed in Jesus of Nazareth. As with the whole story of the Exodus, it is hard to say exactly what happened and whether the plagues took place exactly as described. However, *something* momentous did occur in which God was discerned as the agent of liberation. (See further the Introduction to my booklet *Exodus*: www.peter-sills.co.uk/pilgrimage.)

9   *1.* It is most unlikely that it was the Red Sea that was crossed; it is simply too far away. The location is more likely to have been an inland lake near Goshen where the Israelites were settled.

2. The Bible says the journey took forty years, but this is not to be taken literally. 'Forty years' (or 'forty days') is a biblical expression for a long time, rather like the expression 'a month of Sundays'. It is impossible to say how long the journey actually took, but clearly it was several years.

14   The Babylonian creation myth is the *Enuma Elish* (*circa* 1250 BC). According to this myth the gods issued from Apsu and Tiamat, the

sweet- and salt-water oceans. The elder gods decided to kill the younger gods because of their boisterous behaviour. In the ensuing conflict Marduk emerged as the chief of the younger gods, and demanded as the price of success complete power over the gods. He then caught Tiamat and killed her, and from her corpse created the cosmos.

15   Terah is quoting from the prophet Micah who prophesied two centuries before the Babylonian Exile when the Assyrians were threatening Israel. He, along with others like Isaiah of Jerusalem, denounced the accepted belief that sacrifices would atone for Israel's sins *(Micah 6.6–8)*. What God wanted was repentance, *i.e.* an inner turning away from sin and towards righteous living.

17   1. Isaiah of Babylon does talk about the punishment that Israel has received 'from the Lord's hand' for all her sins *(Isaiah 40.2)*. This represents the way things were seen at the time; the view expressed by Terah represents today's understanding in the light of the love of God revealed by Jesus.

2. There are four so-called 'Servant Songs' in the second part of the Book of Isaiah (chapters 40 – 55). The servant's identity is not altogether clear from the songs: in the first (ch. 41) the prophet seems to be talking about Israel, in the fourth (chs. 52 & 53) about an individual.

20   In ancient Israel, as in other lands, not being able to have children was a source of shame for a woman, and taken as a sign of God's displeasure.

22   Isaiah of Jerusalem lived in the eighth century BC; chapters 1–39 of the Book of Isaiah are based on his words. Second Isaiah (Isaiah of Babylon) lived in the sixth century BC, and chapters 40–55 record his oracles. The remainder of the book comes from later in the sixth century BC. It is the work of several hands, the main contributor is known as 'Third Isaiah'. Isaiah of Babylon was not the only prophet of the Second Exile; Jeremiah and Ezekiel were, perhaps, the most important of the others. Jeremiah was not among those deported to Babylon and remained in Jerusalem. Ezekiel was among the deportees, and his picture of the Valley of the Dry Bones, which are brought back to life, is the most memorable and vivid picture of the restoration of Israel to the Promised Land *(Ezekiel 37.1–14)*.

24   1. *Malachi* 4.5: 'Look, I shall send you the prophet Elijah before the great and terrible day of the Lord comes.'

2. The cloak is a symbol of authority. At the end of his life Elijah was taken up into heaven at the river Jordan. His cloak fell from him, and it was picked up by Elisha, his disciple, who inherited his spirit and continued his work *(2 Kings 2.2–15)*.

36   1. 'Forty days' i.e. a long time: see note 9:2 above.

2. There are three people called James in the NT: (1) James the apostle, one of the sons of Zebedee and brother of John, sometimes referred to as James the Great, who narrates this episode; (2) James, son of Alphaeus, another apostle, known as James the Less; and (3) James of Jerusalem, the brother of Jesus (mentioned by Paul in *Galatians* 1.19), who led the Jerusalem Church after the resurrection and wrote the *Letter of James*. Similarly, there are three Johns in the NT apart from John the Baptist: (1) John the apostle, the other son of Zebedee and brother of James; (2) John the Elder who wrote the three *Letters of John;* and (3) John of Patmos who wrote *Revelation*. (As explained in note 102:2 below, none of these three Johns wrote the *Gospel of John*).

37   The episode to which John refers is at *Mark* 10.35–45.

48   Israel was sometimes referred to by the prophets as the Bride of God, in particular Hosea who refers to Israel as an unfaithful wife, but one whom God is unable to reject (*Hosea ch. 2*).

57   To understand this parable it is necessary to ignore the explanation given in the gospels. Mark's statement that it was given in private to the disciples is accepted device that indicates an editorial addition. While the explanation has value, it is not the meaning Jesus intended as described in the episode.

60   Another example of Jesus breaking convention was his healing of a crippled woman in a synagogue on the sabbath *(Luke 13.10–17)*. He called her 'a daughter of Abraham', an appellation not used in Israel; he touched her in defiance of the holiness code; he spoke to her in public and called her out in the midst of the synagogue, two actions that challenged the primacy of men over women.

66   When Philip told Nathanael they had found the prophet of whom Moses had spoken, Jesus son of Joseph from Nazareth, Nathanael exclaimed, 'Nazareth! Can anything good come from Nazareth?' *(John 1.43–46)*

67   The messianic signs are given by Isaiah: 61.1–3 *(cf. Isaiah 58.6)* For the account of Jesus reading this passage see *Luke 4.18.*

72   John quoted *Micah 6.8* and *Amos 5.24.*

81   Thaddaeus has in mind *Micah 6.9–16.*

83   1. See note 67.

2. Honi HaM'agel (the 'circle-drawer') was a Jewish scholar in the first century BC, and his teachings are the basis of the Mishnah, the first part of the Talmud. During a great drought the people asked him to pray for rain. He drew a circle around himself and told God that he would not move until it rained. So much rain fell that he had to pray again, asking God to end the deluge.

84   See *Isaiah 29.13–14*: 'Because this people worship me with empty words…I shall shock this people yet again, adding shock to shock.'

85   The quotation is from *Isaiah 49.6*, referred to on page 23.

88   The identity of Levi is a puzzle. When Mark records his call (2.14) he says he was the son of Alphaeus, maybe the brother of James the Less (see note 36:2), and not one of the Twelve. I follow Mark; however, in *Matthew 9.9* he is identified with the apostle Matthew.

93   Luke says Jesus told this parable at Jericho after he had called Zacchaeus. I have moved it on a little to Bethphage, the next stop on his journey.

96   *Cf.* Paul who counted all his heritage as a Pharisee as so much loss (or 'garbage') compared with the gain of knowing Christ as Lord *(Philippians 3.8)*.

99   John says that after the feeding Jesus realised that some of the people wanted to seize him and proclaim him king *(John 6.14–15)*, prompting him to withdraw to the hills. His conception of his mission was quite different to popular hopes.

102   1. Belief in the coming of Elijah was well established in Jesus' time, but belief in the resurrection of the dead came late in Judaism. For a long time it was believed that the dead descended to Sheol, the place of shadows. Not long before Jesus' time, when many Israelites had suffered martyrdom at the hands of the Romans, the belief emerged that they would be raised to a new life by God. Whether this belief was true was hotly disputed. It was a point of difference between the Saduccees and the Pharisees *(cf. Acts 23.6–10)*, and it is not surprising that the disciples did not understand Jesus' words.

2. Johanan is the name I have given to the 'Beloved Disciple' mentioned in the *Gospel of John* (e.g. *John 13.23*). He was not one of the Twelve, but like Mary Magdalene was part of the group that accompanied Jesus. He is believed to be the source of the distinctive theology of the Fourth Gospel, which is thought to have been written by another: an unknown member of the community that gathered around the Beloved Disciple. (At some stage the gospel was ascribed erroneously to John the Apostle.) Similarly, the *Gospel of Thomas*, a non-canonical text consisting of the 'hidden' sayings of Jesus, is also by another hand and ascribed to Thomas the Apostle. I have assumed that Thomas the Apostle (who narrates this episode) and Johanan have a similar outlook. However, this is not true of the gospels of *Thomas* and *John*; indeed, some scholars think that *John* may have been written in riposte to *Thomas*.

108   This point is nicely illustrated by the preceding episode in Mark's account. When Jesus was asked: 'Is it lawful for a man to divorce

his wife?' *(Mark 10.1–12)* he did not answer the question, but, characteristically, posed another question in response: 'What did Moses command you?' When the people replied that Moses allowed divorce, Jesus was dismissive, saying that Moses only permitted divorce because they were unteachable. For Jesus, it was not the rule that was important, but God's purpose in the gift of marriage. Marriage creates a new unit of kinship: 'what God has joined together, man shall not separate.' Jesus places the emphasis on the ideal and is impatient with those who ask legalistic questions about the rules. *(NB:* Verses 10–12 are likely to be an editorial addition. The context – a question asked in private – suggests it is additional material: *cf.* note 57.)

114   For the Jericho section of the journey, the story follows the chronology of Luke rather than Mark who says that the meeting with Bartimaeus took place as Jesus left Jericho. Luke places it as Jesus arrives, and adds the encounter with Zacchaeus as he leaves, which Mark omits.

122   The symbolism was important. In ancient times, the choice of mount conveyed a clear message: when a king entered a city in triumph or to subdue it, he rode a horse; when he came in peace he rode a donkey.

123   The action of Jesus cursing a fig tree for not bearing fruit when it is not the season for figs seems completely unreasonable and out of character, and has occasioned much comment (*e.g.* D. E. Nineham, *The Gospel of Saint Mark*, Pelican New Testament Commentaries: Penguin Books, 1963, page 299). The verses about faith and prayer that follow the second part of the story *(vv.* 20–25) seem to have, at best, a tenuous connection with the story which is hardly a good example of prayer being answered!

130   The *Shema* is the basic affirmation of Jewish faith and the central prayer of the Jewish prayer book. It begins with the words, 'Hear, O Israel, the Lord our God is the one Lord…' In his reply to the scribe Jesus quoted the first part of the *shema: Deuteronomy* 6.4–9 *(Mark* 12.29–31).

132   1. I have omitted Chapter 13 of St Mark's Gospel, the so-called Little Apocalypse, from my account. There are good reasons for supposing that it is a later addition to the story, and does not go back to Jesus himself. For example, the reference to the 'abomination of desolation' is generally believed to refer to the statue of himself that the Emperor Caligula set up in the Temple in AD 40. If this is so, the passage must post-date Jesus' ministry and cannot have been spoken by him.

2. The story of the woman who anointed Jesus with perfume has no fixed place in the gospels: Mark and Matthew place it

immediately before the Passion, at the house of Simon the Leper;
Luke places it earlier, in Galilee, at the house of Simon the
Pharisee, adding that the woman wept over Jesus' feet and wiped
them with her hair, and that she had lived an immoral life. He also
adds some pointed teaching about forgiveness. None of these
accounts names the woman. John places the story before the
triumphant entry into Jerusalem, at the house of Lazarus, and
names the woman as Lazarus' sister Mary. He says she anointed
Jesus' feet, rather than his head, and wiped them with her hair. In
some traditions the woman is identified as Mary Magdalene, but
this is unlikely to be correct (like the tradition that she was a
prostitute). I have followed Mark's account, but with John's
identification.

133   The lawyer's response to Jesus' question comes from *Deuteronomy*
6.4–5: 'Hear, O Israel: the LORD is our God, the LORD is our one
God; and you must love the LORD your God with all your heart
and with all your soul and with all your strength.' And from
Leviticus 19.18: 'Never seek revenge or cherish a grudge towards
your kinsfolk; you must love your neighbour as yourself.' The
parable of the Good Samaritan is about the interpretation of the
verse from *Deuteronomy*. 'Kinsfolk' suggests a limited
understanding of 'neighbour', confining it to family, tribe, or
people; Jesus greatly expands this understanding to include
anyone in need, whoever they are and whatever their family, tribe
or people. In effect he re-wrote the law, and, not surprisingly, the
lawyers did not like it and opposed him.

134   The parable of the Lost Son is one of three about forgiveness in
Luke chapter 15 that Jesus told in response to the murmuring
about his table fellowship (the others are the Lost Sheep and the
Lost Coin). Jesus teaches that God's love extends to all, saint or
sinner; his concern is to bring sinners to heaven, not to condemn
them to hell; and he rejoices over those who turn to him and
repent. It is, perhaps, Jesus' concluding refrain that many find hard
to take: 'There will be greater joy in heaven over one sinner who
repents than over ninety-nine righteous people who do not need to
repent.' *(Luke 15.7)*

138   In some versions the two are identified as Peter and John.

140   Also known as James the Less.

155   I have altered the words of the centurion as given by Mark to bring
out their likely meaning. In the gospel they read, 'This man must
have been a son of God,' and are generally taken to be a confession
of faith; the centurion is thought of as the first Gentile convert. This
is unlikely, however nice an ending it provides. As Ched Myers
points out, the centurion later reports to Pilate that Jesus is dead:
'the fact that the man did not defect from his role as a Roman

soldier loyal to Pilate erases the possibility that it is meant by Mark as a *discipleship* story.' (Ched Myers, *Binding the Strong Man,* Orbis Books, 1988 p. 393.) And John Fenton points out that the centurion's statement is consistent with other true statements hurled at Jesus in mockery and not in faith... The most powerful weapon of the torturer is the truth.' (*More About Mark,* SPCK 2001, pp. 64–65) Mark is at pains to bring out the horror and forsakenness of Jesus' death, his utter destruction. For Mark, Jesus' death was not an edifying example of faith and acceptance, as John portrays it, and so it seems much more likely that, in Mark's view, what Longinus meant was, 'Don't tell me he was the Son of God.'

159   The ending of St Mark's Gospel is abrupt: the women 'went out and ran away from the tomb, trembling with amazement. They said nothing to anyone for they were afraid.' But this was not how the story had actually ended, as everyone knew, and from early times it was thought that the original ending had been lost. Two 'proper' endings were added: verses 8b, and 9 – 20 respectively. However, more recent scholarly opinion has moved against the lost ending theory because it is difficult to continue the story after verse 8a without contradiction, hiatus or incoherence. The better opinion is that Mark did indeed conclude his story with the women running away terrified. (*Cf.* John Fenton, *More About Mark,* chapter 7.) However, that does not explain how the news was communicated to others – the conundrum that prompted the 'proper' endings to be written. As we know, the women's experience was shared, and so I continue the story beyond Mark's ending, but in a way, I hope, that respects his account.

162   The story of Peter's boldness confronting the Jewish leaders is told in *Acts* chapter 4, and the story of Cornelius and his family, the first Gentiles to become Christians, in *Acts* chapter 10.

Acknowledgements

Biblical quotations are taken from *The Revised English Bible* copyright © Cambridge University Press and Oxford University Press, 1989. Used by permission.

Picture Credits

The cover and the principal illustrations (pages 2, 28, 76, 98, and 118) are by Philip Kerrey.

The frontispiece is by John Sansom.

The other illustrations come from Pinterest and other sources available on the internet for private use. To the best of my knowledge they are used within the permitted conditions as this book is a private, educational publication and not a commercial venture. If I have unknowingly infringed any copyright, I offer my apologies and will gladly add an acknowledgement on my website and in any future printing. As far as I have been able to ascertain the artists and sources are as follows:

Pages: 10: *Leave your land*; 55: *Who is my mother?* (adapted); 59: *The Sower*; 91: *Feeding 5000*; 137: *Jesus anointed at Bethany*; 150: *Take up your cross* – Annie Valloton, pinterest.com

Page 18: *By the Waters of Babylon* – Lisle Gwynn Garrity; sanctified art.com

Page 25: *John the Baptist* – Erspamer; clipartkey.com

Page 63: *If I just touch him* – Chris Placo; haikudeck.com

Page 73: *Salome* (adapted from an original that I have not been able to trace)

Page 96: *Dives and Lazarus* – Lisa Motley; bible-printables.com

Page 101: *Transfiguration* – clipart-library.com

Page 107: *Healing the Deaf Mute* – diaconos.unblog.fr

Page 116: *Healing Bartimaeus* – Carmelites; ocarm.org

Page 145: *The Arrest of Jesus* – Otto Dix; blog.reformedjournal.com

Page 149: *The Cock Crow* – Robert Leinweber; coloring-pages.info

Page 168: *The Tomb* (adapted) – clipartbest.com

– ALSO BY PETER SILLS –

THE LIFE HIDDEN WITH CHRIST IN GOD

An exploration of what it means to be baptised following the journey of St Paul through Greece. *Illustrated with colour photographs.*

THE TIME HAS COME

A Lenten journey with Saint Mark relating the faith of Jesus to our everyday concerns and the problems of the modern world. Each reflection concludes with a short spiritual exercise.

THEONOMICS

Reconnecting economics with virtue and integrity

A collection of essays examining the way Christian insights can inform and shape economic life. *Principal contributor and co-editor with Andrew Lightbown.*

MÉDARD'S JOURNEY

The journey of two medieval pilgrims to Santiago de Compostela offers food for thought for modern pilgrims and enquirers exploring the spiritual life. *Illustrated with colour photographs.*

LIGHT IN THE DARKNESS

Exploring the path of Christian hope

Drawing out the contrast with the social and economic ideas that shape contemporary life, this exploration presents a distinctive Christian path of hope that integrates the different aspects of life: personal and political, ethical and economic, spiritual and social.

SIGNS, SYMBOLS AND CEREMONIES

A concise exploration of the meaning of Christian worship in five steps, each one including an act of worship designed to let the symbols speak.

– Meditations and Addresses –

A collection of booklets comprising talks given on pilgrimage, meditations for Lent and Advent, and addresses given on other occasions. For the full list of booklets go to: www.peter-sills.co.uk/books, available to download or in print.

All books and booklets can be obtained direct from Peter Sills: www.peter-sills.co.uk